Magnetism and Optics of Molecular Crystals

Magnetism and Optics of Molecular Crystals

J. W. ROHLEDER
Institute of Organic and Physical Chemistry, Technical University of Wrocław, Poland

and

R. W. MUNN
Department of Chemistry, UMIST, Manchester, United Kingdom

JOHN WILEY & SONS
Chichester · New York · Brisbane · Toronto · Singapore

Other Wiley Editorial Offices

John Wiley & Sons, Inc., 605 Third Avenue,
New York, NY 10158-0012, USA

Jacaranda Wiley Ltd, G.P.O. Box 859, Brisbane,
Queensland 4001, Australia

John Wiley & Sons (Canada) Ltd, 22 Worcester Road,
Rexdale, Ontario M9W 1L1, Canada

John Wiley & Sons (SEA) Pte Ltd, 37 Jalan Pemimpin #05-04,
Block B, Union Industrial Building, Singapore 2057

Library of Congress Cataloging-in-Publication Data

Rohleder, J. W.
Magnetism and optics of molecular crystals / J. W. Rohleder and
R. W. Munn.
p. cm.
Includes bibliographical references and index.
ISBN 0 471 93171 3
1. Molecular crystals—Magnetic properties. 2. Molecular
crystals—Optical properties. I. Munn, Robert W. II. Title.
QD940.R64 1992
548—dc20 91-26270
CIP

British Library Cataloguing in Publication Data

A catalogue record for this book is available from the British Library

ISBN 0 471 93171 3

Typeset in Times 10/12pt by
Mathematical Composition Setters Ltd, Salisbury, Wiltshire
Printed and bound in Great Britain by
Biddles Ltd, Guildford, Surrey

Contents

Preface

This book describes the diamagnetic and optical properties of insulating non-absorbing molecular crystals. The emphasis is twofold: on the precise experimental measurement of magnetic susceptibilities and refractive indices, and on the classical interpretation of the results in terms of molecular structure and properties. These are not necessarily the subjects of intense research efforts in themselves, but they often underlie topics which are. For example, spectroscopy and non-linear optics of molecular crystals are both significantly affected by linear optics as outlined here. Our approach is aimed at graduate students and research workers, and we have been selective rather than exhaustive, describing and explaining a smaller number of key methods in detail.

Much of the present material was developed by JWR as graduate lectures. These have been published in Polish by the Technical University of Wrocław (1983) and as a monograph by Panstwowe Wydawnictwo Naukowe, Warsaw (1989). A preliminary English version was prepared by JWR while on leave at the Institute for Materials Research at McMaster University, Hamilton, Ontario, Canada. We are grateful to Professor M. L. Klein and the late Professor J. A. Morrison for suggesting that we should combine to produce this version. We are also grateful to various colleagues, too numerous to mention, for all they have taught us about molecular crystals. Finally we thank Roza and Tricia (respectively) for putting up with us during the prolonged long-range writing of this book.

June 1991

J. W. Rohleder
R. W. Munn

Introduction

Molecular crystals constitute probably the largest class of solids, in view of the millions of distinct chemical compounds known. As such, they constitute a rich and fascinating field of study. Nevertheless, molecular crystals are usually characterized by weak forces between the constituent molecules, which retain their separate identity. The properties of molecular crystals should therefore be explicable in terms of the properties of the molecules and the interactions between them. Conversely, the properties of the molecules should be derivable from the properties of the crystals in suitable cases. This book is concerned with two such cases: the diamagnetism of crystals and the optics of crystals.

Diamagnetism and optics of molecular crystals have received much less attention than they deserve. This contrasts with the existence of several books treating spectroscopy and conduction [1–5], even though these properties are complicated by their sensitivity to crystal imperfections. Diamagnetism and optics can be treated in a rigorous manner which provides an excellent illustration of the effect of crystal symmetry on crystal properties. Furthermore, the analysis of diamagnetism and optics of molecular crystals yields information on molecular properties not readily available by other means, particularly for molecules of low symmetry. A thorough understanding of optical response is also essential to proper study of a variety of energetic, dynamic and spectroscopic properties such as light scattering in molecular crystals.

We therefore hope that the present book will fill a gap in the literature and be useful at several levels. It will provide detailed accounts of the nature, origin and precise measurement of diamagnetism and optics of molecular crystals for researchers in this area. It will also provide background on these topics for workers in related areas. It will be a source of reference on molecular susceptibilities and polarizabilities derived from crystal measurements. And it will exemplify techniques used in the study of molecular crystals for the benefit of students and others new to the area.

In Chapter 1 the most significant properties of second-rank tensors are reviewed for use in the remainder of the book.

The second chapter deals with diamagnetism. So far this is a rather exceptional property of matter where the specific intermolecular interactions can be neglected: the interactions between induced magnetic dipoles are much weaker than all the other forces (van der Waals, charge-transfer interactions, and hydrogen bonding) which keep the molecules together in the form of a piece of crystal. The crystal properties are then those of an oriented gas reflecting the periodicity and geometry of molecular orientation in an ideal crystal whose molecules respond independently.

Paramagnetism and non-linear effects such as ferromagnetism do not offer the same simplifications, and are not considered. We begin by discussing the basic concepts of diamagnetism and go on to describe how the magnetic susceptibility can be measured accurately. The analysis of crystal susceptibilities to yield molecular susceptibilities or magnetizabilities is then treated. The results of such analyses are presented in an extensive tabulation.

The third chapter treats optics. Here the interactions are no longer weak, because of the long range of the potential of an electric dipole, but the form of the interaction is known so that a rigorous treatment can also be formulated. This section begins with a discussion of the basic concepts of optical wave propagation in dielectric crystals with no absorption. We then consider the indicatrix and methods for the accurate measurement of optical birefringence. The oriented gas model is no longer adequate, and it becomes necessary to treat the local electric field responsible for polarizing the molecules, which arises not only from the applied field of the light wave but also from the fields of the induced dipole moments of the molecules. Our aim will again be to obtain an understanding of the macroscopic properties of the molecular crystal in terms of the properties of constituent molecules and their arrangement in the crystallographic unit cell. This is of course parallel to our aim in Chapter 2—the magnetic and optical properties are those which are at present best understood (compared, for example, with electronic transport phenomena). Understanding the optical properties proves the more difficult, however, because the molecular response is large and local field effects must be treated. On the other hand, an understanding of the optical properties provides insight into various spectroscopic and energetic properties, such as intensities of lattice vibrational spectra and energies of charged states. A mo lecular interpretation of the optical properties also serves to provide a means of analysing the temperature dependence of crystal birefringences, which contain information about molecular reorientation at and near a crystal phase transformation. The analysis of crystal refractive properties is again supplemented by a table of derived molecular polarizabilities. Up to this stage the treatment is restricted to linear response, but extensions to optically non-linear materials are discussed in the last section.

REFERENCES

1. F. Gutman and L. E. Lyons, *Organic Semiconductors*, Wiley, New York, 1967.
2. D. P. Craig and S. H. Walmsley, *Excitons in Molecular Crystals*, Benjamin, New York, 1968.
3. A. S. Davydov, *Theory of Molecular Excitons*, Plenum, New York, 1971.
4. E. A. Silinsh, *Organic Molecular Crystals: Their Electronic States*, Springer, Berlin, 1980.
5. M. Pope and C. E. Swenberg, *Electronic Processes in Organic Crystals*, Clarendon, Oxford, 1982.

1 Tensors and Symmetry

1.1 DEFINITIONS

In describing the properties of materials one must differentiate between scalar, vector and tensor properties. Scalars and vectors are in common use but it is worth while to recall briefly some results of tensor algebra of importance in later sections. The equations will be given here without proof; for more details the reader is referred to more specialized monographs listed at the end of the chapter [1–4].

There are various definitions of a tensor. A very useful formulation frequently met in the area of chemical physics of solids is as follows. Suppose we are given two vectors: $\boldsymbol{q}$ (independent variable) and $\boldsymbol{p}$ (dependent variable), each having three components which are defined in an orthogonal right-handed system of axes $x_1x_2x_3$. Then *any factor* $\boldsymbol{T}$ *relating these two vectors* by an equality

$$\boldsymbol{p} = \boldsymbol{T}\boldsymbol{q} \tag{1.1.1}$$

is called a tensor.

In particular, $\boldsymbol{T}$ can be a scalar, which is then also called a zero-rank tensor. In such a case vectors $\boldsymbol{p}$ and $\boldsymbol{q}$ are parallel to each other. Frequently, $\boldsymbol{T}$ denotes a quantity composed of nine components arranged in a 3×3 array and called a *second-rank* tensor. In index notation equality (1.1.1) then reads

$$p_i = \sum_{j=1}^{3} T_{ij}q_j, \qquad (i = 1, 2, 3) \tag{1.1.2}$$

or in matrix notation

$$\begin{pmatrix} p_1 \\ p_2 \\ p_3 \end{pmatrix} = \begin{pmatrix} T_{11} & T_{12} & T_{13} \\ T_{21} & T_{22} & T_{23} \\ T_{31} & T_{32} & T_{33} \end{pmatrix} \begin{pmatrix} q_1 \\ q_2 \\ q_3 \end{pmatrix} \tag{1.1.3}$$

In general, vector $\boldsymbol{p}$ in (1.1.3) is no longer parallel to $\boldsymbol{q}$ except for special and important cases which will be reported later. Equations of the type (1.1.1) are very popular in physics, e.g. $\boldsymbol{p} = \boldsymbol{\alpha E}$, where $\boldsymbol{p}$ is an electric dipole moment induced by the electric field $\boldsymbol{E}$ in a molecule whose polarizability is given by the tensor $\boldsymbol{\alpha}$; and $\boldsymbol{j} = \boldsymbol{\sigma E}$, where $\boldsymbol{j}$ is the density of the electric current induced by the field $\boldsymbol{E}$ in an anisotropic material having the electric conductivity $\boldsymbol{\sigma}$. Second-rank tensors typically represent *material constants* of a crystal whose symmetry is lower than cubic. In the rest of Chapter 1 we will be exclusively concerned with second-rank tensors, which dominate in Chapters 2 and 3.

A general, or *unsymmetric* tensor $\boldsymbol{T}$ can be uniquely resolved into *symmetric* $\boldsymbol{T}^{(s)}$ and *anti-symmetric* $\boldsymbol{T}^{(a)}$ parts

$$\boldsymbol{T} = \boldsymbol{T}^{(s)} + \boldsymbol{T}^{(a)} \tag{1.1.4}$$

with the components of $\boldsymbol{T}^{(a)}$ and $\boldsymbol{T}^{(s)}$ defined so that

$$\begin{aligned} T_{ij}^{(s)} &= T_{ji}^{(s)} \\ T_{ij}^{(a)} &= -T_{ji}^{(a)} \end{aligned} \tag{1.1.5}$$

Notice that all diagonal components of an antisymmetric tensor disappear.

From (1.1.4) and (1.1.5) we have

$$T_{ij} = T_{ij}^{(s)} + T_{ij}^{(a)}$$

and

$$T_{ji} = T_{ji}^{(s)} - T_{ji}^{(a)}.$$

Hence

$$\begin{aligned} \boldsymbol{T}^{(s)} &= \begin{pmatrix} T_{11} & \frac{1}{2}(T_{12}+T_{21}) & \frac{1}{2}(T_{13}+T_{31}) \\ & T_{22} & \frac{1}{2}(T_{23}+T_{32}) \\ & & T_{33} \end{pmatrix}, \\ \boldsymbol{T}^{(a)} &= \begin{pmatrix} 0 & \frac{1}{2}(T_{12}-T_{21}) & \frac{1}{2}(T_{13}-T_{31}) \\ & 0 & \frac{1}{2}(T_{23}-T_{32}) \\ & & 0 \end{pmatrix}. \end{aligned} \tag{1.1.6}$$

Symmetric tensors contain six independent components. This is just the amount of information which is necessary to describe the dimensions of the graphical representation of the tensor and fix its orientation in space. Anti-symmetric second-rank tensors have three independent non-zero components and are frequently used as matrices to describe the rotation of a coordinate axis system in three-dimensional space.

1.2 TRANSFORMATION OF TENSOR COMPONENTS

We have already mentioned that the values of the components of a tensor, T_{ij}, are bound to the particular choice of the system of reference axes, $x_1x_2x_3$. A change of this system will, in general, also involve a change of T_{ij} values.

Two systems of reference axes, $x_1x_2x_3$ and $x_1'x_2'x_3'$, each orthogonal and right-handed, can be brought into coincidence by means of a combination of the two simple operations:

(1) A translation of $x_1x_2x_3$ that leaves the axes parallel, i.e. $x_1 \parallel x_1'$, $x_2 \parallel x_2'$, $x_3 \parallel x_3'$. Such an operation does not change the components of a vector, nor does it change the components of a tensor.

(2) A rotation in space of $x_1x_2x_3$ about its origin. The relation between the two systems of axes can be expressed by means of a unitary matrix c_{ij} such that

$$\text{Det } \boldsymbol{c} = +1$$

where Det denotes the determinant of matrix $\boldsymbol{c}$, with components that are the cosines of the angles between primed and unprimed axes:

$$c_{ij} = \cos(x_i', x_j). \tag{1.2.1}$$

Denoting by $\boldsymbol{R}$ a vector with components (x_1, x_2, x_3) we have

$$\boldsymbol{R}' = \boldsymbol{cR} \tag{1.2.2}$$

where $\boldsymbol{R}'$ is the same vector in the primed system of axes and its components are (x_1', x_2', x_3'). It is well known that equation (1.2.2) gives the *transformation law* of a vector and that the length of the vector is an *invariant* of the transformation

$$|\boldsymbol{R}'| = |\boldsymbol{R}|.$$

The reciprocal transformation can be written in the form

$$\boldsymbol{R} = \boldsymbol{c}^{-1}\boldsymbol{R}' = \boldsymbol{c}^{\mathrm{T}}\boldsymbol{R}' \tag{1.2.3}$$

where $\boldsymbol{c}^{\mathrm{T}}$ denotes $\boldsymbol{c}$ transposed.

It may easily be shown on substituting (1.2.3) into equation (1.1.1) that the transformation law for second-rank tensor components has the form

$$\boldsymbol{T}' = \boldsymbol{cTc}^{\mathrm{T}}. \tag{1.2.4}$$

Frequently for $\boldsymbol{T}'$ another character is used, e.g. $\boldsymbol{\tau}$.

Transformation (1.2.4) does not change the *trace* or the sum of diagonal components

$$\text{Tr } \boldsymbol{T} = T_{11} + T_{22} + T_{33} \tag{1.2.5}$$

which is then the invariant of the transformation

$$\text{Tr } \boldsymbol{T}' = \text{Tr } \boldsymbol{T}. \tag{1.2.6}$$

This property of a tensor is due to the fact that $\boldsymbol{c}$ is a unitary matrix. The reciprocal transformation to (1.2.4) reads

$$\boldsymbol{T} = \boldsymbol{c}^{\mathrm{T}}\boldsymbol{T}'\boldsymbol{c}. \tag{1.2.7}$$

The transformation laws have importance because they reflect the intrinsic properties of physical quantities. For this reason they may also serve as a basis for the classification of physical properties, leading to the following types:

(1) A zero-rank tensor or scalar s is a quantity whose value does not change upon translation or rotation of the system of coordinate axes, i.e.

$$s' = s. \tag{1.2.8}$$

Hence a scalar is itself an invariant of the transformation.

(2) A first-rank tensor or vector A is a physical quantity whose components change upon rotation of the system of axes according to an equation

$$A' = \boldsymbol{c}\mathbf{A}. \tag{1.2.9}$$

The length of A is an invariant of the transformation.

(3) A second-rank tensor is a physical quantity that transforms according to an equation

$$\boldsymbol{T}' = \boldsymbol{c}^{\mathrm{T}}\boldsymbol{T}\boldsymbol{c}. \tag{1.2.10}$$

The invariance of the trace leads to the definition of the *mean value* of a tensor which is then one-third of its trace

$$\langle T \rangle = \tfrac{1}{3}\,\mathrm{Tr}\,\boldsymbol{T}. \tag{1.2.11}$$

The mean value of a tensor physical quantity is what we obtain in an experiment where the sample consists of fine grains of the material (or is a fluid).

1.3 GRAPHICAL REPRESENTATION

Suppose we are given nine coefficients S_{ij} for i and j running from 1 to 3. Then the equation

$$\sum_i \sum_j S_{ij}x_ix_j = 1 \tag{1.3.1}$$

or, expanding under the assumption that $S_{ij} = S_{ji}$,

$$S_{11}x_1^2 + S_{22}x_2^2 + S_{33}x_3^2 + 2S_{12}x_1x_2 + 2S_{13}x_1x_3 + 2S_{23}x_2x_3 = 1 \tag{1.3.2}$$

means that we are considering all points $P(x_1x_2x_3)$ which satisfy this equation. An ensemble of such points forms a three-dimensional quadratic surface which can be an ellipsoid, a paraboloid or a hyperboloid depending on the signs of the coefficients S_{ii}; a classification will be given later. Equation (1.3.2) describing such a surface (which always has a centre of symmetry) can also be written in the matrix form

$$\boldsymbol{r}^{\mathrm{T}}\boldsymbol{S}\boldsymbol{r} = 1 \tag{1.3.3}$$

where $\boldsymbol{S}$ is the symmetric matrix of the coefficients S_{ij} and $\boldsymbol{r}$ is a vector from the centre of symmetry to a point on the surface.

It can easily be shown that on changing the coordinate system of axes the S_{ij} coefficients will change in a manner identical to that for tensor components

$$\boldsymbol{S}' = \boldsymbol{c}\boldsymbol{S}\boldsymbol{c}^{\mathrm{T}},$$

where $\boldsymbol{c}$ is the matrix relating the new system of axes to the original. Therefore, the equation

$$\boldsymbol{r}^{\mathrm{T}}\boldsymbol{T}\boldsymbol{r} = 1 \tag{1.3.4}$$

is a graphical representation of the tensor $\boldsymbol{T}$, called the *representation quadric*.

Among the infinite number of systems of coordinate axes $x_1'x_2'x_3'$, there is always one and only one system $X_1X_2X_3$ for which all off-diagonal terms disappear

$$x_1x_2x_3 \rightarrow X_1X_2X_3 \Rightarrow T_{ij} = 0 \qquad \text{for } i \neq j. \tag{1.3.5}$$

These particular axes X_i are called *principal axes* of the tensor $\boldsymbol{T}$ and the values along X_i, denoted by T_i, are the *principal values* or *principal components* of $\boldsymbol{T}$. Methods to transform a tensor to its principal axes and to determine its principal values are described in the monograph of Nye [1].

Now the classification of quadric surfaces can easily be formulated:

(1) If all T_i are positive (or all are negative) the quadric has the form of a triaxial ellipsoid given by the equation

$$\frac{X_1^2}{A_1^2} + \frac{X_2^2}{A_2^2} + \frac{X_3^2}{A_3^2} = \pm 1 \tag{1.3.6}$$

where the coefficients

$$A_i = T_i^{-1/2} \tag{1.3.7}$$

are the lengths of the semi-axes.

(2) If one of the principal values is negative the quadric has the form of a hyperboloid of one sheet, Figure 1.1a.

(3) If two of the principal values are negative the quadric has the form of a paraboloid of two sheets.

There is also another means which is frequently used to obtain a representative surface of a tensor. Suppose we are given a unit vector $\boldsymbol{l}$ chosen in an arbitrary direction. The product $(\boldsymbol{T} \cdot \boldsymbol{l})$ is then another vector, in general not parallel to $\boldsymbol{l}$. To obtain its component along $\boldsymbol{l}$ we just need to make the scalar product $\boldsymbol{l} \cdot (\mathbf{T} \cdot \boldsymbol{l})$ or, in matrix notation

$$T_l = \boldsymbol{l}^{\mathrm{T}} \boldsymbol{T} \boldsymbol{l}. \tag{1.3.8}$$

Expression (1.3.8) gives a scalar which is called the *tensor value in the direction* $\boldsymbol{l}$. On expanding we have

$$T_l = (l_1 \ l_2 \ l_3) \begin{pmatrix} T_{11} & T_{12} & T_{13} \\ T_{21} & T_{22} & T_{23} \\ T_{31} & T_{32} & T_{33} \end{pmatrix} \begin{pmatrix} l_1 \\ l_2 \\ l_3 \end{pmatrix}. \tag{1.3.9}$$

Choosing $\boldsymbol{l}$ for all directions in space we obtain successive points T_l which together form the *surface of magnitude* of $\boldsymbol{T}$. The shape and meaning of such a surface differ completely from those of the representation quadric, as Figure 1.1b shows.

In particular, in the principal system of axes $X_1X_2X_3$, where $\boldsymbol{T}$ has a diagonal form, the unit vectors along the axes X_i have the components $(1, 0, 0)$, $(0, 1, 0)$ and $(0, 0, 1)$. We then have

$$T_{X1} = (1 \quad 0 \quad 0) \begin{pmatrix} T_1 & 0 & 0 \\ 0 & T_2 & 0 \\ 0 & 0 & T_3 \end{pmatrix} \begin{pmatrix} 1 \\ 0 \\ 0 \end{pmatrix} = T_1, \tag{1.3.10}$$

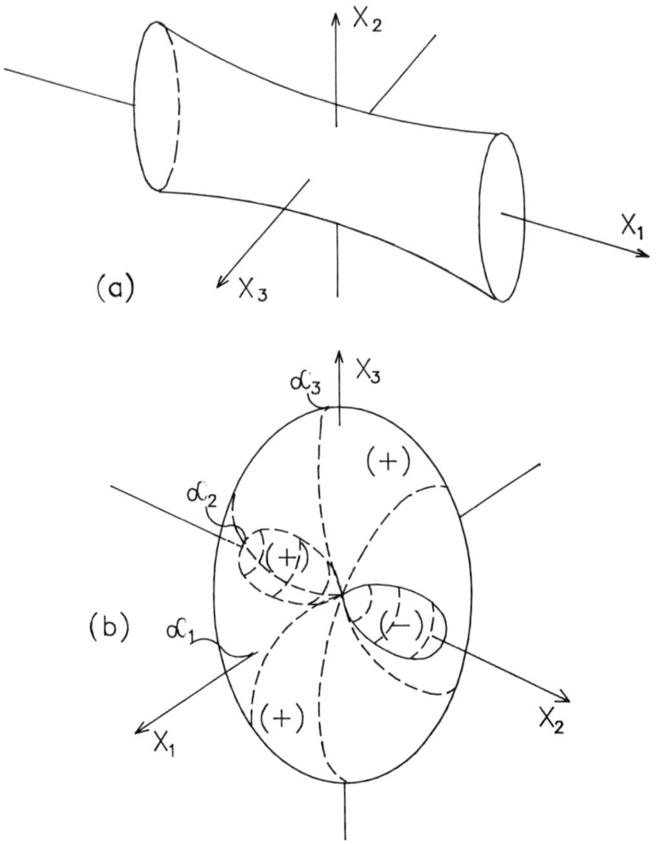

Figure 1.1. (a) Representation quadric for one principal value negative; (b) surface of magnitude for the same case, showing the marked difference

and similarly $T_{X2} = T_2$, $T_{X3} = T_3$. Hence we see that along the principal axes the tensor components are equal to the principal values, as required.

Keeping $\boldsymbol{l}$ within a particular plane we obtain from (1.3.8) a set of points forming a line which describes the *section of the tensor* with that particular plane. For example, if we choose $\boldsymbol{l} = (\cos\phi, \sin\phi, 0)$, then the various points (ϕ, T_l) give us a tensor section perpendicular to the X_1 axis; ϕ is then the angle measured from X_1. Note that all $\boldsymbol{l}$s start from the point $(0, 0, 0)$; therefore, the tensor section is in this case a *central* section.

Equation (1.3.8) can be rewritten in the form

$$\boldsymbol{Tl} = T_l \boldsymbol{l}. \qquad (1.3.11)$$

We may now ask whether there are $\boldsymbol{l}$s which satisfy this new equation, or, in other words, whether vector $(\boldsymbol{Tl})$ can be parallel to $\boldsymbol{l}$. As is well known, in each system of reference axes $x_1x_2x_3$ there are three and only three such directions,

$l_1 \parallel X_1$, $l_2 \parallel X_2$, $l_3 \parallel X_3$, identical with the principal axes of $\boldsymbol{T}$. They can be found algebraically by solving an equation of the third degree, or by the method of successive approximations; details of the calculation are given in [1]. From the directions of the principal axes the principal values can be calculated on substituting the ls into (1.3.8). Notice that for each l_i we can write $\boldsymbol{q}_i = |\boldsymbol{q}|\, l_i$. For vectors $\boldsymbol{p}_i$ we then obtain from (1.1.1)

$$\begin{aligned} \boldsymbol{p}_i &= \boldsymbol{T}\boldsymbol{q}_i \\ &= |\boldsymbol{q}_i|\, \boldsymbol{T} l_i \\ &= |\boldsymbol{q}_i|\, T_i l_i, \end{aligned} \tag{1.3.12}$$

and we see that vector $\boldsymbol{p}_i$ is parallel to $\boldsymbol{q}_i$. In other words, the direction of the 'effect' is parallel to the external 'cause' when applied in one of the principal directions of the crystal. The directions of the principal axes of the quadric are identical with those of the surface of magnitude.

1.4 ASPECTS OF CRYSTAL SYMMETRY

The description of the physical properties of a crystal necessarily involves considerations of the symmetry which the idealized fully periodic structure of that crystal possesses. This is not only the problem of how matter is distributed over a three-dimensional lattice. As we shall see later, atoms or molecules may be replaced by vectors or ellipsoids of magnitude representing microscopic counterparts of the macroscopic physical quantity. It is then a general problem to give an interpretation at the molecular level of a given macroscopic property of a periodic structure.

In the following it will be useful to treat four symmetry groups.

(1) The *crystallographic space group* G_l comprises all symmetry operations which transform every point, line or plane in the crystal lattice into another point, line or plane which is indistinguishable from the original one and has identical surroundings. It is G_l which describes the periodic arrangement of matter in a crystal lattice and which is quoted in crystallographic papers.

(2) The *unit-cell group* or *factor group* G_c contains all the symmetry operations of G_l apart from primitive translations given by the vector

$$\boldsymbol{t} = n_1\boldsymbol{a}_1 + n_2\boldsymbol{a}_2 + n_3\boldsymbol{a}_3, \tag{1.4.1}$$

where the n_i are integers and the $\boldsymbol{a}_i$ are the edges of the unit cell (which need not be primitive). The unit-cell group need not be a point group because it may include screw axes and glide planes which do not fix any point in space and because its symmetry elements need not all intersect in one point. Now the translational symmetry of the crystal lattice means that any vector or tensor representing a physical property of an infinite crystal must have the same components at all translationally equivalent points. (The restriction to an infinite crystal allows us to neglect special surface effects such as the difference in electric field at the surface of a polarized crystal from that in its interior.) Therefore the symmetry of the physical properties of crystals is determined by the unit-cell group, which is accordingly of particular importance.

(3) The *site group* G_s consists of all symmetry operations which leave invariant both the crystal and one particular site. It is simultaneously a subgroup of G_l and of G_c, and is clearly a point group. It is usually assumed that the symmetry of a molecule in a crystal is that of the site group for the molecular centre of mass. Though not necessarily exactly true, this proves a good approximation.

(4) The *interchange group* G_i for a particular site consists of those symmetry operations of G_c not contained in G_s for the site in question, except for the identity operation required to satisfy the group axioms. The interchange group contains all symmetry operations required to generate all sites crystallographically equivalent to the chosen site, and hence need not be a point group. Although G_s and G_i may refer to any site in the unit cell, in practice we shall be concerned with sites occupied by molecular centres of mass.

To illustrate these definitions we take the orthorhombic space group *Pbca*, aspects of the symmetry of which are shown in Figure 1.2. We shall use the notation for symmetry operations introduced by Seitz [5]. In this notation $\{A \mid s\}$ represents a point group operation A and a translation vector $\boldsymbol{s}$, so that this operation acting on a vector $\boldsymbol{r}$ yields [6]

$$\{A \mid s\}\boldsymbol{r} = A\boldsymbol{r} + \boldsymbol{s} \tag{1.4.2}$$

and the group multiplication rule is

$$\{A_1 \mid s_1\}\{A_2 \mid s_2\} = \{A_1A_2 \mid A_1s_2 + s_1\}. \tag{1.4.3}$$

The space group *Pbca* corresponds to a lattice produced by three-dimensional translations of a unit cell which has three glide planes corresponding to the operations

$$\{\sigma_x \mid \tfrac{1}{2}\ \tfrac{1}{2}\ 0\},\ \{\sigma_y \mid 0\ \tfrac{1}{2}\ \tfrac{1}{2}\} \text{ and } \{\sigma_z \mid \tfrac{1}{2}\ 0\ \tfrac{1}{2}\}.$$

Here σ_x corresponds to a mirror reflection perpendicular to the x axis, and $f_1f_2f_3$ to a translation vector $f_1\boldsymbol{a}_1 + f_2\boldsymbol{a}_2 + f_3\boldsymbol{a}_3$ (so that f_i is the fraction of the unit-cell edge a_i in the translation). Then using (1.4.2), the new position $x'y'z'$ produced by the operation of the first glide plane perpendicular to the x (or a) axis on a point xyz is given by

$$\begin{pmatrix} x' \\ y' \\ z' \end{pmatrix} = \begin{pmatrix} -1 & 0 & 0 \\ 0 & 1 & 0 \\ 0 & 0 & 1 \end{pmatrix} \begin{pmatrix} x \\ y \\ z \end{pmatrix} + \begin{pmatrix} \frac{1}{2} \\ \frac{1}{2} \\ 0 \end{pmatrix}$$

$$= \begin{pmatrix} \frac{1}{2} - x \\ \frac{1}{2} + y \\ z \end{pmatrix}. \tag{1.4.4}$$

In addition to the glide planes, the space group *Pbca* contains two other operations, the identity $\{E \mid 000\}$ and the centre of symmetry $\{C_i \mid 000\}$, both

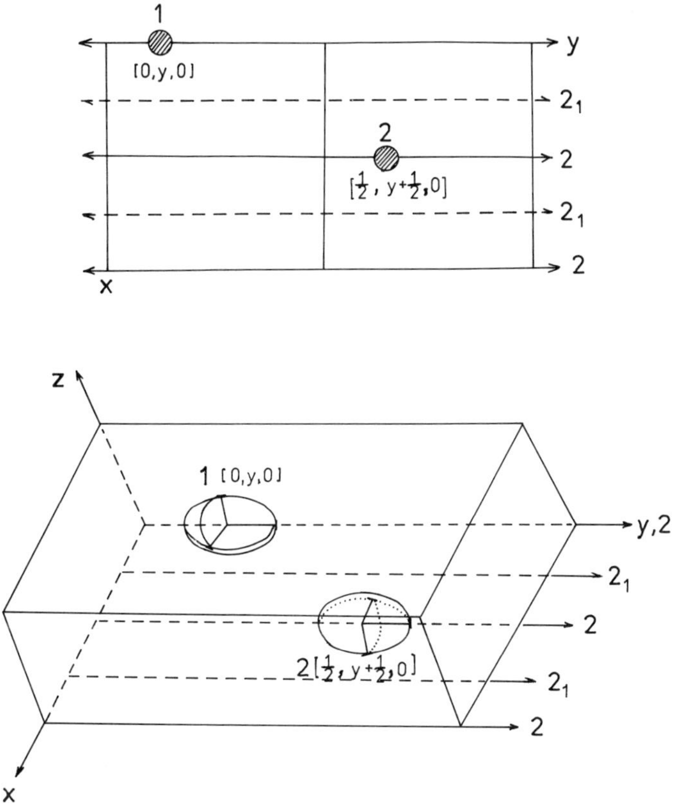

Figure 1.2. 'Oriented gas' of molecular tensors in a *Pbca* unit cell

having zero translational component. Combining the centre of symmetry with the glide planes using (1.4.3) then generates a set of twofold screw axes, for example

$$\{C_i\,|\,000\}\{\sigma_y\,|\,0\ \tfrac{1}{2}\ \tfrac{1}{2}\} = \{\sigma_y\,|\,0\ \tfrac{1}{2}\ \tfrac{1}{2}\}\{C_i\,|\,000\} = \{C_{2y}\,|\,0\ \tfrac{1}{2}\ \tfrac{1}{2}\}, \tag{1.4.5}$$

where C_{2y} denotes a twofold axis parallel to y (or b). Then altogether the unit-cell group G_c contains the eight elements $\{E\,|\,000\}$, $\{C_i\,|\,000\}$, $\{\sigma_x\,|\,\frac{1}{2}\ \frac{1}{2}\ 0\}$, $\{\sigma_y\,|\,0\ \frac{1}{2}\ \frac{1}{2}\}$, $\{\sigma_z\,|\,\frac{1}{2}\ 0\ \frac{1}{2}\}$, $\{C_{2x}\,|\,\frac{1}{2}\ \frac{1}{2}\ 0\}$, $\{C_{2y}\,|\,0\ \frac{1}{2}\ \frac{1}{2}\}$ and $\{C_{2z}\,|\,\frac{1}{2}\ 0\ \frac{1}{2}\}$.

Now a *Pbca* unit cell can be filled with matter in two different ways [7]. One possibility has molecules of no particular symmetry placed at arbitrary or general positions. In this case the site group G_s reduces to the identity operation $\{E\,|\,000\}$ and the interchange group G_i is identical with the unit-cell group G_c. The operations of G_i then lead to a total of eight molecules in the unit cell in general positions. The alternative possibility has centrosymmetric molecules placed (necessarily) at centrosymmetric sites; an example is benzene. In this case the site group G_s comprises the identity $\{E\,|\,000\}$ and the centre of symmetry $\{C_i\,|\,000\}$. The interchange group G_i is then of order four and hence generates four molecules in the unit cell. The elements of G_i can be selected from the identity, the glide planes and the screw axes in a number of ways, but the choice

$$\{E\,|\,000\},\ \{C_{2x}\,|\,\tfrac{1}{2}\ \tfrac{1}{2}\ 0\},\ \{C_{2y}\,|\,0\ \tfrac{1}{2}\ \tfrac{1}{2}\}\ \text{ and }\ \{C_{2z}\,|\,\tfrac{1}{2}\ 0\ \tfrac{1}{2}\}$$

has the advantage of preserving the handedness of sets of coordinate axes [8]. Notice that the distinction between these two cases arises only because we can distinguish between bonded and non-bonded atoms: as far as symmetry is concerned, a centrosymmetric molecule is a repeating motif equivalent to a pair of unsymmetrical molecules related by a centre of symmetry.

1.5 SYMMETRY RESTRICTIONS OF TENSOR COMPONENTS

From the considerations of the preceding section we arrive at the following conclusions. First, owing to the translational symmetry of the lattice, any tensor property $\boldsymbol{T}$ of a crystal can be obtained from that of a single unit cell. Second, the contributions $\boldsymbol{t}$ of the different molecules contained in the unit cell are related by the operations of the interchange group excluding their translational component. (If the crystal contains molecules not related by symmetry, then the independent molecules together constitute the repeating motif so that their contributions have to be added.) And third, the molecular tensor $\boldsymbol{t}$ for a given site must be invariant under all operations of the site group G_s.

This last conclusion is a molecular counterpart of Neumann's principle that macroscopic crystal properties must have the symmetry of the point group of the unit cell [1] and similarly determines those elements of $\boldsymbol{t}$ which must be zero or equal to others in the crystal environment. Suppose that G_s comprises n symmetry operations specified by the matrices $\boldsymbol{A}_i$, $i=1,\dots n$. Then the invariance principle requires that for any $p=1,\dots n$

$$\boldsymbol{t}=\boldsymbol{A}_p\boldsymbol{t}\boldsymbol{A}_p^{\mathrm{T}}. \tag{1.5.1}$$

Except for rotations C_n with $n>2$, a simple scheme to deduce the symmetry constraints on $\boldsymbol{t}$ is obtained by denoting all the elements in the starting tensor $\boldsymbol{t}$ on the right-hand side of (1.5.1) by plus signs. For a mirror plane perpendicular to the crystallographic b axis, equation (1.5.1) then requires

$$\begin{pmatrix}+&+&+\\+&+&+\\+&+&+\end{pmatrix}=\begin{pmatrix}1&0&0\\0&-1&0\\0&0&1\end{pmatrix}\begin{pmatrix}+&+&+\\+&+&+\\+&+&+\end{pmatrix}\begin{pmatrix}1&0&0\\0&-1&0\\0&0&1\end{pmatrix}$$

$$=\begin{pmatrix}+&-&+\\-&+&-\\+&-&+\end{pmatrix}. \tag{1.5.2}$$

We can see that four elements of $\boldsymbol{t}$ change sign under the transformation (irrespective of their initial sign and magnitude). If $\boldsymbol{t}$ is to be invariant under the transformation, it follows at once that these elements must be zero by symmetry, i.e. $t_{12} = 0 = t_{21}$ and $t_{23} = 0 = t_{32}$. Using this scheme one finds that a twofold axis of symmetry parallel to the crystallographic axis b imposes no further constraints on $\boldsymbol{t}$, while the identity and centre of symmetry have no effect on any symmetric second-rank tensor. The operations σ_y, C_{2y}, E and C_i make up the C_{2h} point group, and so we arrive at the conclusion that the invariant tensor for a molecule occupying a site of C_{2h} symmetry is of the form

$$\boldsymbol{t}^{(s)} = \begin{pmatrix} t_{11} & 0 & t_{13} \\ 0 & t_{22} & 0 \\ t_{31} & 0 & t_{33} \end{pmatrix} \tag{1.5.3}$$

where the superscript denotes the site invariance. The symmetry (1.5.3) also applies to a site of C_{2v} symmetry. With another orientation of the symmetry elements (the mirror plane or the twofold axis) certain other elements of $\boldsymbol{t}$ become equal to zero but there are always four components that disappear in this site group symmetry.

However, axes C_n with $n > 2$ interchange some elements of $\boldsymbol{t}$ instead of at most changing their sign. For example, a fourfold axis parallel to the crystallographic c axis leads to the transformation

$$\begin{pmatrix} 0 & 1 & 0 \\ -1 & 0 & 0 \\ 0 & 0 & 1 \end{pmatrix} \begin{pmatrix} t_{11} & t_{12} & t_{13} \\ t_{21} & t_{22} & t_{23} \\ t_{31} & t_{32} & t_{33} \end{pmatrix} \begin{pmatrix} 0 & -1 & 0 \\ 1 & 0 & 0 \\ 0 & 0 & 1 \end{pmatrix} = \begin{pmatrix} t_{22} & -t_{21} & t_{23} \\ -t_{12} & t_{11} & -t_{13} \\ t_{32} & -t_{31} & t_{33} \end{pmatrix}. \tag{1.5.4}$$

In this case the principle of equivalence leads to the equalities $t_{11} = t_{22}$, $t_{12} = -t_{21} = -t_{12}$, $t_{13} = t_{23} = -t_{13}$, $t_{32} = -t_{31} = -t_{32}$, whence

$$\boldsymbol{t}^{(s)} = \begin{pmatrix} t_{11} & 0 & 0 \\ 0 & t_{11} & 0 \\ 0 & 0 & t_{33} \end{pmatrix}. \tag{1.5.5}$$

Then $\boldsymbol{t}$ has the symmetry of an ellipsoid of rotation with its unique axis parallel to c.

Notice that the form of $\boldsymbol{t}^{(s)}$ is determined by the symmetry of the site occupied by the molecule in the crystal and not by the symmetry of the isolated molecule. In practice, the forces in molecular crystals are frequently weak enough to make it a reasonable assumption that $\boldsymbol{t}^{(s)}$ has the same symmetry as in the free molecule; in such cases it is possible to determine molecular constants from crystal data. However, it should be borne in mind that specific crystal effects such as conformational changes, hydrogen bonding or charge transfer may make the assumption unreliable.

1.6 ORIENTED GAS MODEL

In the molecular-kinetic description of an ideal gas we assume that the gas phase consists of *point-like* and *non-interacting* atoms or molecules. Similarly, in the *oriented gas* model a crystal is approximated as an ensemble of non-interacting molecules whose dimensions are not significant. However, in contrast to a gas, the molecules in a crystal do have an *orientation* fixed in space if the thermal motion is neglected. Depending on the problem under consideration we can assign to each molecule a vector or a tensor corresponding to the molecular property which related to the macroscopic property of the crystal. The crystal property is then obtained by summing the molecular vectors or tensors over all molecules in the crystal.

As we can see, such a formulation of the model is based upon a severe simplification. Nevertheless, even in this simple form it was used (more or less explicitly) with success in solving problems such as the following:

(1) Determination of the resultant electric moment of a ferroelectric crystal as a sum of oriented molecular dipoles.

(2) Calculation of the spectroscopic dichroic ratio, i.e. the absorption anistropy of a crystal along its principal optic directions.

(3) Foundation of the molecular basis of diamagnetism in molecular crystals which may be helpful in investigating unresolved structures.

(4) Structural investigations of crystal-to-crystal phase transformations.

(5) Investigations of the influence of temperature on the changes of physical properties of crystals.

Irrespective of the fact that vectors or tensors are to be added to form the macroscopic property, their translational invariance in an ideally periodic structure greatly facilitates the problem: it is sufficient to take into consideration just a single unit cell. But it should be borne in mind that the addition of molecular quantities must be carried out in a system of coordinate axes common to the microscopic and macroscopic quantities. The most simple choice is related to the principal axes of the crystal tensor $\boldsymbol{\tau}$; however, most frequently an orthogonal crystallographic system is chosen which reflects the basic symmetry elements of the crystal space group. This is because the symmetry operations are valid in this system of axes, although in general neither $\boldsymbol{\tau}$ nor $\boldsymbol{t}$ has a diagonal form in this system.

As a consequence of the simplifications made within the model, there are certain restrictions in its applicability to solve physicochemical problems. For example, one would not expect it to give a good result in the description of the elasticity or the lattice dynamics of crystals, as in these problems the spatial extension and interactions of the molecules play an essential role. However, as will be discussed in Chapter 2, in suitable cases we can show that the molecular tensor in a lattice of weakly interacting molecules differs only slightly from that of a free molecule. This effect may be understood as reflecting the influence of intermolecular forces on the symmetry and/or the shape of molecules.

The crystal axes in which the macroscopic or crystal tensor $\boldsymbol{\tau}$ is given will be specified by the orthogonal unit vectors, $\boldsymbol{a}_\alpha$, $\alpha = 1, 2, 3$. The details of this choice depend on what convention is accepted in the particular area of application; they will be specified separately in Chapters 2 and 3.

The diagonal form of $\boldsymbol{\tau}$, denoted by $\boldsymbol{T}$, is obtained in its principal axes X_i, $i = 1, 2, 3$. If we write $g_{i\alpha} = \cos(X_i, \boldsymbol{a}_\alpha)$ then we have

$$\boldsymbol{\tau} = \boldsymbol{g}^{\mathrm{T}}\boldsymbol{T}\boldsymbol{g}. \tag{1.6.1}$$

$\boldsymbol{T}$ is also a macroscopic quantity.

Molecular tensors $\boldsymbol{t}$ are given in a molecular set of axes bound to each molecule k and formed by orthogonal unit vectors $\boldsymbol{l}_A(k)$, $A = 1, 2, 3$. The orientation of the molecular axes relative to the crystal axes is then given by direction cosine matrices $\boldsymbol{c}(k)$ with elements

$$c_{A\alpha}(k) = \boldsymbol{l}_A(k) \cdot \boldsymbol{a}_\alpha, \qquad k = 1, 2, \ldots Z \tag{1.6.2}$$

where Z is the number of molecules in the unit cell. Thus A is represented by row A in the matrix $\boldsymbol{c}(k)$.

Suppose we have the direction cosine matrix $\boldsymbol{c}(1)$ for the first molecule in the unit cell. The matrix $\boldsymbol{c}(k)$ for a symmetry-related molecule k can be obtained from $\boldsymbol{c}(1)$ by a transformation using one of the symmetry operations in the interchange group G_{i}. For this purpose the translational part of the operation can be ignored, and then the orientational part can be specified by the matrix $\boldsymbol{B}(k)$ which transforms any vector $\boldsymbol{r}$ into its symmetry-related counterpart $\boldsymbol{r}'$ by $\boldsymbol{r}' = \boldsymbol{B} \cdot \boldsymbol{r}$. It is the rows of $\boldsymbol{c}(1)$ which represent the axes and hence the columns of the transpose matrix $\boldsymbol{c}(1)^{\mathrm{T}}$, so that we obtain $\boldsymbol{c}(k)$ from

$$\boldsymbol{c}(k)^{\mathrm{T}} = \boldsymbol{B}(k) \cdot \boldsymbol{c}(1)^{\mathrm{T}}. \tag{1.6.3}$$

If A_p is a matrix corresponding to one of the operations of the site group G_{s}, then the site invariant molecular tensor (superscript s) is obtained by performing the transformations

$$\boldsymbol{t}^{(\mathrm{s})} = \boldsymbol{A}_p \boldsymbol{t} \boldsymbol{A}_p^{\mathrm{T}} \tag{1.6.4}$$

for all $p = 1, 2, \ldots s$ in turn. $\boldsymbol{t}^{(\mathrm{s})}$ has a common form for each site; its contribution to the crystal tensor $\boldsymbol{\tau}$ is given by

$$\boldsymbol{t}^{(\mathrm{s})}(k) = \boldsymbol{c}(k)^{\mathrm{T}}\boldsymbol{t}^{(\mathrm{s})}\boldsymbol{c}(k).$$

Here the transformation (1.2.4) has been used, taking account of how $\boldsymbol{c}(k)$ is defined. However, the contributions $\boldsymbol{t}^{(\mathrm{s})}(k)$ are symmetry dependent according to (1.6.3), so we need to know $\boldsymbol{t}^{(\mathrm{s})}(k)$ only for the first molecule, for which $\boldsymbol{c}(1)$ may be given in crystallographic papers:

$$\boldsymbol{t}^{(\mathrm{s})}(1) = \boldsymbol{c}(1)^{\mathrm{T}}\boldsymbol{t}^{(\mathrm{s})}\boldsymbol{c}(1). \tag{1.6.5}$$

The mean of the contributions of all Z molecules in the unit cell is then given by

$$\boldsymbol{\tau} = Z^{-1} \sum_{k=1}^{Z} \boldsymbol{t}^{(s)}(k)$$

$$= Z^{-1} \sum_{k=1}^{Z} \boldsymbol{c}(k)^{\mathrm{T}} \boldsymbol{t}^{(s)} \boldsymbol{c}(k)$$

or, using (1.6.1), (1.6.3) and (1.6.5),

$$\boldsymbol{g}^{\mathrm{T}} \boldsymbol{T} \boldsymbol{g} = \boldsymbol{\tau}$$

$$= Z^{-1} \sum_{k=1}^{Z} \boldsymbol{B}(k) \boldsymbol{t}^{(s)}(1) \boldsymbol{B}(k)^{\mathrm{T}} \qquad (1.6.6)$$

Equation (1.6.6) expresses the oriented gas model in the crystal axes. The contribution of the first molecule

$$t_{\alpha\beta}^{(s)}(1) = c_{\alpha A}(1) t_{AB}^{(s)} c_{B\beta}(1) \qquad (1.6.7)$$

for a given crystal needs to be calculated just once. The repeated Greek or capital Roman subscripts are understood to be summed over the values 1, 2 and 3 (Einstein convention). Note how the use of different types of letter for crystal and molecular axes helps to avoid error in writing (1.6.7) and similar equations when repeated subscripts are put adjacent; there is no need to specify whether $\boldsymbol{c}$ or $\boldsymbol{c}^{\mathrm{T}}$ is the first factor.

1.7 REFERENCES

1. J. F. Nye, *Physical Properties of Crystals*, Clarendon, Oxford, 1957.
2. W. A. Wooster, *Tensors and Group Theory for the Physical Properties of Crystals*, Clarendon, Oxford, 1973.
3. W. Rubinowicz, *Wektory i Tensory*, Polskie Towarzystwo Matematyczne, Warszawa–Wrocław, 1950.
4. Y. I. Ssirotin and M. P. Shasskolskaya, *Osnovy Kristallofiziki*, Nauka, Moskva, 1979.
5. F. Seitz, *Ann. Math.*, **37**, 17 (1936).
6. J. C. Decius and R. M. Hexter, *Molecular Vibrations in Crystals*, McGraw-Hill, New York, 1977.
7. *International Tables for X-Ray Crystallography*, Volume 1, Kynoch Press, Birmingham, 1974.
8. E. R. Bernstein, S. D. Colson, R. Kopelman and G. W. Robinson, *J. Chem. Phys.*, **48**, 5596 (1968).

2 Diamagnetism

2.1 BASIC CONCEPTS

Investigation of the properties of diamagnetic solids became more widespread after Krishnan's work in 1933 (see [13]) on the magnetic anisotropy. It soon became clear that such measurements can serve as a rich source of information on magnetic properties of molecules. They may help to elucidate crystal structures with a rather large number of weakly diffracting atoms in the unit cell, particularly organic molecular crystals. Nowadays the status of structural investigations has changed significantly, with the development of automated X-ray diffractometers and powerful structural refinement techniques, so that diamagnetic measurements are no longer needed to assist in crystal structure determinations.

However, the direct relationship between crystal and molecular diamagnetism still leaves a number of interesting applications of diamagnetic measurements. First, they provide experimental data for comparison with theoretical studies of the magnetic properties of molecules. Recent *ab initio* calculations remain unsatisfactory, and further calculations require the stimulus of more experimental data. Secondly, magnetic studies can contribute much to the investigation of the mechanism of the subtle phase transformations common in molecular crystals. At temperatures near such a transition, organic crystals give rather few X-ray reflections, mostly of low intensity, so that only gross changes of structure can readily be studied. However, the direct relationship between molecular and crystal diamagnetic anisotropy means that even a small change in molecular orientation can be reflected in a considerable change in crystal diamagnetic anisotropy. Thirdly, a better understanding of the magnetic properties of conventional molecular crystals is likely to help the understanding of the ordering induced in liquid crystals by strong magnetic fields. Finally we note the pedagogical value of studying diamagnetic properties of molecular crystals as an introduction to the oriented gas model and the effects of crystal symmetry, which also find application in other properties such as optics.

Before providing any description of magnetic or electrical properties, it is necessary to consider what type of system of units is to be used. In the early development of the subject it was customary to use an unrationalized system with three base units, such as cgs–emu. Modern practice is to use a rationalized system with four base units, especially SI units. We shall normally use equations compatible with SI units, but some numerical data will be given in a form more directly comparable with older results, with appropriate conversion factors.

The field vector which determines the force on a current element is the magnetic induction $\boldsymbol{B}$, units $\mathrm{T} = \mathrm{V\,s\,m^{-2}} = \mathrm{Wb\,m^{-2}}$ ($= 10^4$ gauss). Current i circulating uniformly around an area S gives rise to a magnetic moment $m = iS$, units $\mathrm{A\,m^2}$. More generally, a magnetic moment is associated with any charged particle having angular momentum, whether due to motion or to spin (internal angular momentum). Materials subject to a magnetic induction experience a change in magnetic moment; the magnetic moment per unit volume is the magnetization $\boldsymbol{I}$, units $\mathrm{A\,m^{-1}}$. For present purposes only materials with no permanent magnetic moment are considered, so that the magnetization is entirely induced by the magnetic induction. Magnetic equations are often found to adopt simpler forms in terms of the auxiliary magnetic field vector $\boldsymbol{H}$ such that

$$\boldsymbol{H} = \boldsymbol{B}/\mu_0 - \boldsymbol{I} \quad \text{or} \quad \boldsymbol{B} = \mu_0(\boldsymbol{H} + \boldsymbol{I}). \tag{2.1.1}$$

Here μ_0 is the permeability of free space, defined to equal $4\pi \times 10^{-7}\ \mathrm{H\,m^{-1}}$ ($\mathrm{Wb\,A^{-1}\,m^{-1}}$), and $\boldsymbol{H}$ clearly has the same dimensions as $\boldsymbol{I}$.

The material properties determine the relationship between the magnetization and the magnetic induction or magnetic field. If we exclude systems exhibiting hysteresis, then for sufficiently small fields $\boldsymbol{I}$ depends linearly on $\boldsymbol{H}$:

$$\boldsymbol{I} = \boldsymbol{\Psi} \cdot \boldsymbol{H}. \tag{2.1.2}$$

Here $\boldsymbol{\Psi}$ is the second-rank 'volume' *magnetic susceptibility tensor*, which is a dimensionless material constant independent of $\boldsymbol{H}$. Its elements Ψ_{ij} in cartesian coordinates form a 3×3 matrix, which consideration of the energy of magnetization shows to be symmetric, i.e. $\Psi_{ji} = \Psi_{ij}$, so that

$$\boldsymbol{\Psi} = \begin{pmatrix} \Psi_{11} & \Psi_{12} & \Psi_{13} \\ \Psi_{12} & \Psi_{22} & \Psi_{23} \\ \Psi_{13} & \Psi_{23} & \Psi_{33} \end{pmatrix}. \tag{2.1.3}$$

Then the components I_i of the magnetization are obtained from (2.1.2) as

$$I_i = \Psi_{i1}H_1 + \Psi_{i2}H_2 + \Psi_{i3}H_3. \tag{2.1.4}$$

This shows that in general the magnetization is not parallel to the magnetic field unless the off-diagonal elements of $\boldsymbol{\Psi}$ are zero; conditions under which this occurs are treated later.

Substitution of (2.1.2) in (2.1.1) yields

$$\boldsymbol{B} = \mu_0(\boldsymbol{1} + \boldsymbol{\Psi}) \cdot \boldsymbol{H} \tag{2.1.5}$$

$$= \mu_0 \boldsymbol{\mu} \cdot \boldsymbol{H}, \tag{2.1.6}$$

where $\boldsymbol{1}$ is the 3×3 unit tensor and $\boldsymbol{\mu}$ is the *magnetic permeability tensor*. Experiment shows that the components of $\boldsymbol{\Psi}$ are typically 10^{-5} or less. The diagonal components of $\boldsymbol{\mu}$ are therefore dominated by those of $\boldsymbol{1}$, so that it is customary to deal with $\boldsymbol{\Psi}$ itself rather than $\boldsymbol{\mu}$. A further consequence is that

$$\boldsymbol{B} \approx \mu_0 \boldsymbol{H} \tag{2.1.7}$$

so that $\boldsymbol{B}$ and $\boldsymbol{H}$ are parallel and

$$\boldsymbol{I} \approx (\boldsymbol{\Psi}/\mu_0)\boldsymbol{B}. \tag{2.1.8}$$

Although Ψ is dimensionless, its value does change between different systems of units depending on rationalization. In particular, $\Psi_{\text{SI}} = 4\pi\Psi_{\text{emu}}$. Other magnetic susceptibilities are also encountered. The *mass susceptibility* $\boldsymbol{\varkappa}$ is given by

$$\boldsymbol{\varkappa} = \boldsymbol{\Psi}/\rho \tag{2.1.9}$$

where ρ is the density. This relates the magnetic moment per unit mass to the magnetic field, and is convenient for treating solutions prepared by weighing. Mass susceptibilities in SI and emu are related by $\varkappa_{\text{SI}}/\text{m}^3\,\text{kg}^{-1} = 4\pi \times 10^{-3}\,\varkappa_{\text{emu}}/\text{cm}^3\,\text{g}^{-1}$. The *molar susceptibility* $\boldsymbol{\chi}$ is given by

$$\boldsymbol{\chi} = \boldsymbol{\varkappa} M = \boldsymbol{\Psi} M/\rho \tag{2.1.10}$$

where M is the molar mass. This relates the magnetic moment per unit amount of substance to the magnetic field; being simply proportional to the molecular magnetizability, it is of direct theoretical importance. Molar susceptibilities in SI and emu are related by $\chi_{\text{SI}}/\text{m}^3\,\text{mol}^{-1} = 4\pi \times 10^{-6}\,\chi_{\text{emu}}/\text{cm}^3\,\text{mol}^{-1}$.

As we have seen, the magnetic susceptibility forms a second-rank (3×3) tensor. The ellipsoid of magnitude given by the equation

$$\boldsymbol{r}^{\text{T}} \cdot \boldsymbol{\chi} \cdot \boldsymbol{r} = \sum_{i,j} (r_i \chi_{ij} r_j) = -1 \tag{2.1.11}$$

and shown in Figure 2.1 has three principal values χ_1, χ_2, χ_3 in the principal system of axes X_1, X_2, X_3 (cf. Section 1.3). They are not vectors, so in figures they will be indicated as line segments. For a diamagnetic crystal all χ_i are negative; no case is known so far in which the principal values differ in sign. Therefore, the graphic representation of (2.1.11) is a triaxial ellipsoid. Each point P on that surface gives the value χ_n of the susceptibility in the direction determined by the unit vector $\boldsymbol{n}$

$$\chi_n = \boldsymbol{n}^{\text{T}} \cdot \boldsymbol{\chi} \cdot \boldsymbol{n} \tag{2.1.12}$$

or, in the principal axis system,

$$\chi_n = \chi_1 n_1^2 + \chi_2 n_2^2 + \chi_3 n_3^2 \tag{2.1.13}$$

where $n_i = \cos(\boldsymbol{n}, X_i)$.

The magnetic susceptibility determines the behaviour of a substance in an inhomogeneous magnetic field, which can serve as a method of measurement. When the magnetic induction acting on a body of magnetic moment $\boldsymbol{m}$

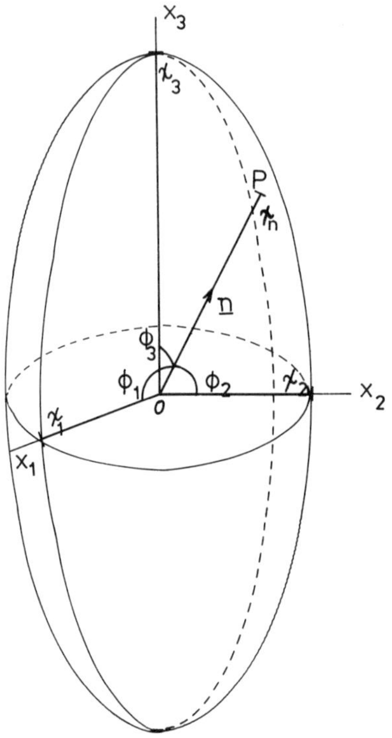

Figure 2.1. Value χ_n of the susceptibility in the direction of the unit vector $\boldsymbol{n}$

changes by d$\boldsymbol{B}$, the energy changes by $\mathrm{d}W = -\boldsymbol{m} \cdot \mathrm{d}\boldsymbol{B}$. If the volume of the body is V, then equations (2.1.2) and (2.1.7) lead to

$$\mathrm{d}W = -\mu_0 V\boldsymbol{H} \cdot \boldsymbol{\Psi} \cdot \mathrm{d}\boldsymbol{H}. \tag{2.1.14}$$

Thus in a uniform field W is constant, but if $\boldsymbol{H}$ varies in space, so does W. This means that the body is subject to a force tending to move it to a region where its energy is lower, i.e. to larger $\boldsymbol{H}$ for Ψ positive and to smaller $\boldsymbol{H}$ for Ψ negative. Since the magnitude and sign of the force depend on the susceptibility, this phenomenon provides a means of measuring Ψ (see following subsection). It also yields a classification of magnetic substances [1–9].

Diamagnetic substances have Ψ negative and small (typically of the order of 10^{-6}), independent of magnetic field and practically independent of temperature. Most pure organic and inorganic substances in all phases belong to this class, e.g. water, benzene, sodium chloride, and certain metals such as copper and lead. It is with such substances that this section is concerned.

Paramagnetic substances have Ψ positive and typically of the order of 10^{-6} to 10^{-4}. This class has subdivisions according to the origin and temperature dependence of the paramagnetism. *Insulating paramagnetics* have a reciprocal susceptibility which varies linearly with temperature according to the Curie or Curie–Weiss law. This class comprises ions and molecules containing unpaired electrons, e.g. transition metal, lanthanide and actinide salts, and free radicals and odd-electron molecules such as diphenylpicrylhydrazine (DPPH), oxygen (O_2) and nitrogen(II) oxide (NO). *Metallic paramagnetics* have a susceptibility which depends only weakly on temperature and is of the order of 10^{-6}. It originates in the conduction electrons (Pauli paramagnetism) in metals like Na and Al. *Antiferromagnetics* have a susceptibility which goes through a maximum at the Néel temperature, owing to the presence of oppositely oriented sublattices of cancelling spins. Examples are MnO and MnS.

Ferromagnetics have very high susceptibilities (10^3 to 10^4) which depend on temperature, on the magnetic field, and on the magnetic, thermal and mechanical history of the sample. Above the Curie temperature ferromagnetics become normal paramagnetics. This behaviour is associated with the iron group of metals (Fe, Ni, Co) and some of their alloys. *Ferrimagnetics* or ferrites are a subgroup which display a different temperature dependence of the susceptibility attributable to the presence of sublattices of opposed but not cancelling spins.

It should be noted that this classification of magnetic materials is based on the observed properties. One also meets theoretical statements about, for example, diamagnetic and paramagnetic contributions to the susceptibility, but these contributions cannot be separated experimentally and their relative sizes depend on the choice of gauge in any calculation [10]. Calculations of the separate diamagnetic and paramagnetic contributions in a given gauge are therefore useful mainly in comparisons of different substances rather than for the absolute values.

2.2 MEASUREMENT OF MEAN MAGNETIC SUSCEPTIBILITY

The most widespread and accurate method for the determination of the mean magnetic susceptibility is the *Gouy method* [11]. It can be used to examine isotropic or polycrystalline substances, or finely powdered anisotropic substances.

The substance under investigation is placed in a glass ampoule of uniform cross-section suspended from one end of a balance in an inhomogeneous magnetic field (see Figure 2.2). The lower end of the sample is in a field H and the upper end in the much smaller field H_0. If the substance is diamagnetic, the ampoule will experience a force pulling it into places with smaller field strength and diminishing its apparent weight. The balance can be restored by a gravitational or electromagnetic force. To quantify the effect we ignore any effects of anisotropy, which in the case of an anisotropic substance requires very fine pulverization.

The magnetic field acting on the sample varies with the vertical position z, and from equation (2.1.14) this causes a varying energy, i.e. a force. The

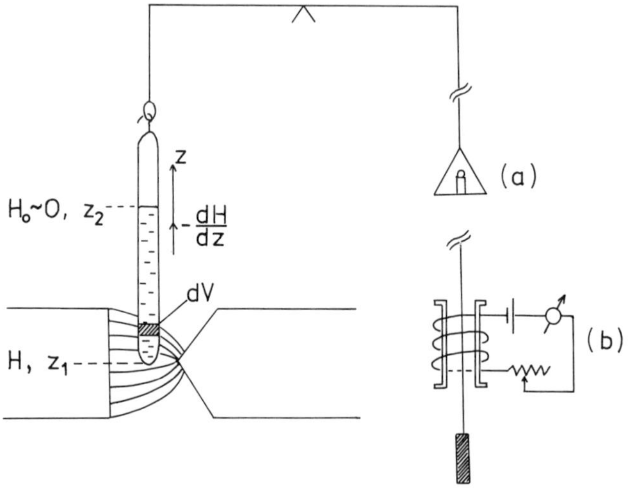

Figure 2.2. Method of measurement of the mean magnetic susceptibility, $\langle\chi\rangle$

element of force acting on a volume element $A\,\mathrm{d}z$, where A is the inner cross-sectional area of the ampoule, is

$$\mathrm{d}F_z = -\mathrm{d}W/\mathrm{d}z. \tag{2.2.1}$$

For an effectively isotropic sample of mean susceptibility $\langle\Psi\rangle$, equation (2.1.14) then yields

$$\mathrm{d}F_z = \mu_0 A\langle\Psi\rangle H\,\mathrm{d}H. \tag{2.2.2}$$

On integrating between the two ends of the sample, z_1 and z_2, we obtain the force acting on the whole sample:

$$\begin{aligned} F_z &= \int_{z_1}^{z_2} \mu_0 A\langle\Psi\rangle H\,\mathrm{d}H \\ &= \tfrac{1}{2}\mu_0 A\langle\Psi\rangle (H_0^2 - H^2). \end{aligned} \tag{2.2.3}$$

If the field H_0 can be neglected compared with H, the force is approximately

$$F_z = -\tfrac{1}{2}\mu_0 A\langle\Psi\rangle H^2. \tag{2.2.4}$$

The minus sign corresponds to the fact that the force acting on a substance with a negative mean susceptibility is directed away from the region of high field H.

To achieve good precision with the Gouy method, the sample should be no shorter than 15 cm, with a diameter of 2–3 cm just a little smaller than the gap between the pole pieces of the magnet. Accuracy can be increased by making comparative measurements with a reference substance such as water placed in the same ampoule in the same place in the field. This minimizes

Table 2.1. Susceptibility of distilled water, according to [1]

$t/^{\circ}C$	1	10	30	70
$-\Psi \times 10^6$	0.7189	0.720	0.722	0.724

errors associated with variations in the geometry of the experiment. The susceptibilities of 1 cm^3 pure water at various temperatures are given in Table 2.1. For the most accurate results it is also necessary to purge the air from the ampoule with nitrogen or hydrogen; owing to its oxygen content air has a small positive susceptibility of $\Psi_{emu} \approx 0.029 \times 10^{-6}$ ($\Psi_{SI} \approx 0.4 \times 10^{-6}$) at room temperature.

The Gouy method is simple and accurate but has the disadvantage that it measures the volume susceptibility $\langle \Psi \rangle$, whereas usually the mass susceptibility $\langle \varkappa \rangle$ or the molar susceptibility $\langle \chi \rangle$ is required. For fluids the conversion is straightforward, but for powders the relation between mass and volume is more troublesome, requiring rigorous standardization of the sample preparation procedure. A review of other experimental methods is given by Bates [8]. Of these, the *Faraday method* does not suffer from this disadvantage and also allows much smaller samples to be used (less than 100 mg).

In the Faraday method, the pole pieces of the electromagnet are shaped in such a way that the product $H(\partial H/\partial z)$ is constant along the suspension direction. With this configuration, the force is constant at different levels z in the sample and it is therefore not necessary to integrate over the whole volume. As a result, the Faraday method gives the mass susceptibility directly. Instrumental details of this method and its use for samples weighing up to 20 mg at temperatures between 5 and 300 K are given by Morris [12]. This paper also describes methods for eliminating errors associated with the electrostatic forces which often arise when powdered non-conducting substances are handled.

2.3 MEASUREMENT OF SUSCEPTIBILITY ANISOTROPY

The susceptibility anisotropy can be measured by suspending a crystalline sample in a homogeneous magnetic field. Both static and dynamic methods are available, each depending on the torque on the sample, which we consider first. We suppose that the (diamagnetic) crystal is suspended on a thin filament and that a homogeneous magnetic field is applied perpendicular to the filament. Let the suspension direction be parallel to the principal axis of the susceptibility tensor corresponding to the principal susceptibility Ψ_2 (see Figure 2.3). Then the two other susceptibilities Ψ_1 and Ψ_3 lie in the horizontal plane containing $\boldsymbol{H}$. We suppose $|\Psi_1| > |\Psi_3|$, and then mechanical

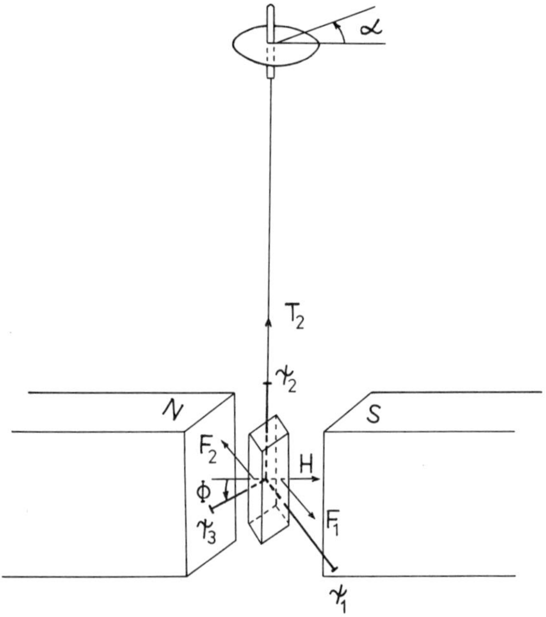

Figure 2.3. Diamagnetic crystal in the homogeneous magnetic field in a non-equilibrium position

equilibrium is reached when the direction of Ψ_3 is parallel to $\boldsymbol{H}$ and Ψ_1 perpendicular to $\boldsymbol{H}$.

Suppose now that the equilibrium is disturbed by a small rotation α of the upper end of the filament; owing to the elasticity of the filament, the crystal will rotate in the same direction but by a smaller angle ϕ (see Figure 2.3). In the new equilibrium position the crystal will be subject to the two parallel restoring forces F_1 and F_2. The resulting torque $\boldsymbol{T}$ depends on the induced magnetic dipole moment of the crystal $\boldsymbol{m}$ and on the field strength:

$$\boldsymbol{T} = \mu_0 \boldsymbol{m} \wedge \boldsymbol{H}. \qquad (2.3.1)$$

The magnetization $\boldsymbol{I}$ of a crystal of volume V is $\boldsymbol{m}/V$ and is given by equation (2.1.2), so that

$$\begin{aligned} \boldsymbol{m} &= V\boldsymbol{I} \\ &= V\boldsymbol{\Psi} \cdot \boldsymbol{H}. \end{aligned} \qquad (2.3.2)$$

We need the component of the torque about the suspension direction T_2, which is obtained as

$$\begin{aligned} T_2 &= \mu_0(m_3 H_1 - m_1 H_3) \\ &= \mu_0 V(\Psi_3 - \Psi_1) H_1 H_3, \end{aligned} \qquad (2.3.3)$$

where H_i is the component of $\boldsymbol{H}$ parallel to the principal component Ψ_i. As shown in Figure 2.4, these components satisfy

$$H_1 = H \sin \phi, \qquad H_3 = H \cos \phi. \tag{2.3.4}$$

(The fact that Ψ_3 and H_3 have opposite directions is of no significance because Ψ_3 is not a vector.) Using equation (2.1.10) to express Ψ in terms of the molar susceptibility χ as $\rho\chi/M$, ρ being the density and M being the molar mass, and noting that ρV is the mass w of the suspended crystal, we obtain

$$T_2 = \tfrac{1}{2}\mu_0(w/M)(\chi_3 - \chi_1)H^2 \sin 2\phi. \tag{2.3.5}$$

Thus in this simple case the torque depends on the difference of the principal susceptibilities in the plane perpendicular to the suspension direction. This difference determines the anisotropy in a given crystal section. Suspension along the three principal directions in turn gives torques which are proportional to the various anisotropies and can serve to determine them experimentally [13,14]. In reviewing some of the experimental methods below, we shall assume for simplicity that the principal directions are known. When this is not so, typically for samples of irregular shape without a cleavage plane to facilitate crystallographic identification, the methods determine an anisotropy $\Delta\chi$ given as follows.

Suppose that the sample is suspended in an arbitrarily chosen direction perpendicular to the magnetic field as before. A laboratory system of axes xyz is then chosen with z parallel to the suspension and directed upwards, x parallel to the magnetic field, and y perpendicular to x and z so as to complete a right-handed system. Unit vectors parallel to x, y and z are denoted $\boldsymbol{i}$, $\boldsymbol{j}$ and $\boldsymbol{k}$ respectively, cf. Figure 2.5. In general, the horizontal xy central section of the susceptibility ellipsoid will be an ellipse. Then in the magnetic field the crystal will tend to assume a position in which the shorter axis of the ellipse lies parallel to $\boldsymbol{H}$ and the longer axis perpendicular to $\boldsymbol{H}$. Therefore in the equilibrium torque-free state the vector $\boldsymbol{i}$ lies parallel to the shorter axis and

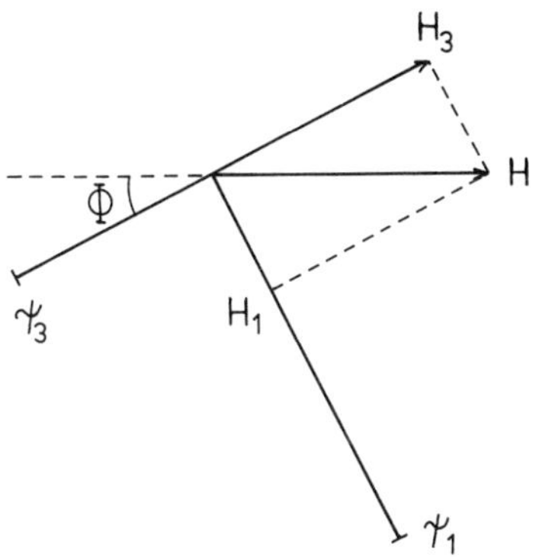

Figure 2.4. Field components along principal crystal susceptibilities corresponding to Figure 2.3

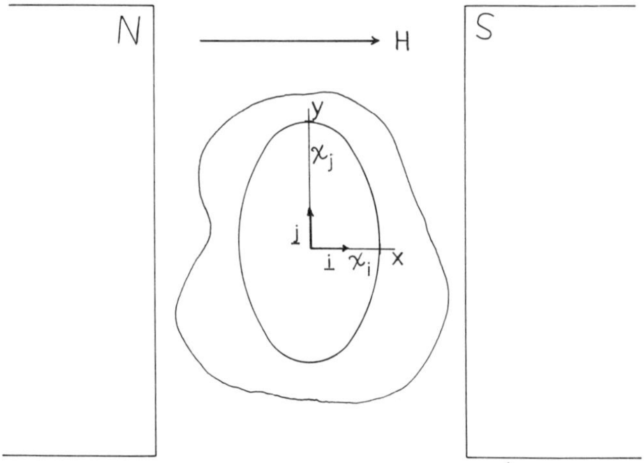

Figure 2.5. Equilibrium position of a sample with unknown principal directions of $\boldsymbol{\chi}$ in the *xy*-section

$\boldsymbol{j}$ parallel to the longer. The anisotropy $\Delta\chi$ in the xy section is the difference between the values of the susceptibility in the directions of the two axes of the ellipse, which is $\chi_i - \chi_j$ in terms of the quantity χ_n defined in Figure 2.1. Using equation (2.1.12) we obtain

$$\Delta\chi = \boldsymbol{i}^{\mathrm{T}} \cdot \boldsymbol{\chi} \cdot \boldsymbol{i} - \boldsymbol{j}^{\mathrm{T}} \cdot \boldsymbol{\chi} \cdot \boldsymbol{j}. \tag{2.3.6}$$

Whether or not the principal directions are known, the anisotropies alone do not suffice to determine the individual components of $\boldsymbol{\chi}$. This is achieved by combining measurements of the anisotropy with the mean susceptibilities $\langle\chi\rangle$ already treated. In the general case described by equation (2.3.6), there are six independent components of $\boldsymbol{\chi}$ to be determined and hence five independent anisotropies. Solving the equations for the components can then be cumbersome but is always feasible. In practice, accurate results require least-squares fitting to an overdetermined set of anisotropies.

Let us now return to measurements of the anisotropy, beginning with static techniques. In mechanical equilibrium, the torque T_2 exerted by the magnetic field is balanced by the torque T_2' exerted by the elasticity of the filament from which the sample is suspended. For the arrangement illustrated in Figure 2.3, the elastic torque is given by

$$T_2' = k(\alpha - \phi), \tag{2.3.7}$$

where $\alpha - \phi$ is the twist in the filament and k the torsional modulus of the filament. Equating this torque with T_2 given by equation (2.3.5) yields

$$\tfrac{1}{2}\mu_0(w/M)(\chi_3 - \chi_1)H^2 \sin 2\phi = k(\alpha - \phi) \tag{2.3.8}$$

or

$$\alpha - \phi = A(\chi_3 - \chi_1)\sin 2\phi, \tag{2.3.9}$$

where $A = \mu_0 w H^2 / 2Mk$. For a thin quartz filament, α usually considerably exceeds ϕ (which is conveniently indicated by a small mirror which reflects a light beam on to a scale). Then α becomes a linear function of sin 2ϕ, and a least squares fit to a series of observations of ϕ at increasing α gives $(\chi_3 - \chi_1)$ with good accuracy, given k [15].

Eventually, increasing the twist angle of the filament α will increase ϕ to a critical value $\phi_{max} = \pi/4$. Any further increase in α, however small, will then result in a rapid rotational motion of the crystal. If the critical value of α is α_{cr} when ϕ assumes its maximum value $\pi/4$, so that sin $2\phi_{max} = 1$, then (2.3.9) yields

$$\chi_3 - \chi_1 = (\alpha_{cr} - \pi/4)/A. \qquad (2.3.10)$$

Thus the anisotropy can also be determined from a measurement of α_{cr} [14], provided the modulus k is known.

The modulus can be determined directly with either experimental method using a standard material such as calcite ($CaCO_3$), whose principal susceptibilities and their directions are well known. The crystal has trigonal symmetry and its morphology provides an easy means of recognizing the principal directions. The threefold axis passes through a corner where three crystal edges meet at equal obtuse angles $\delta = 103^\circ$ (see Figure 2.6). One principal susceptibility χ_3 must be parallel to this direction, and the perpendicular section of the susceptibility ellipsoid is isotropic with $\chi_1 = \chi_2$; the values of the emu susceptibilities are [16]

$$\chi_1 = \chi_2 = -36.3 \times 10^{-6}\ \mathrm{cm^3\,mol^{-1}}$$
$$\chi_3 = -40.5 \times 10^{-6}\ \mathrm{cm^3\,mol^{-1}}.$$

(The conversion to SI units is

$$\chi_{SI}/\mathrm{m^3\,mol^{-1}} = 4\pi \times 10^{-6} \chi_{emu}/\mathrm{cm^3\,mol^{-1}}.)$$

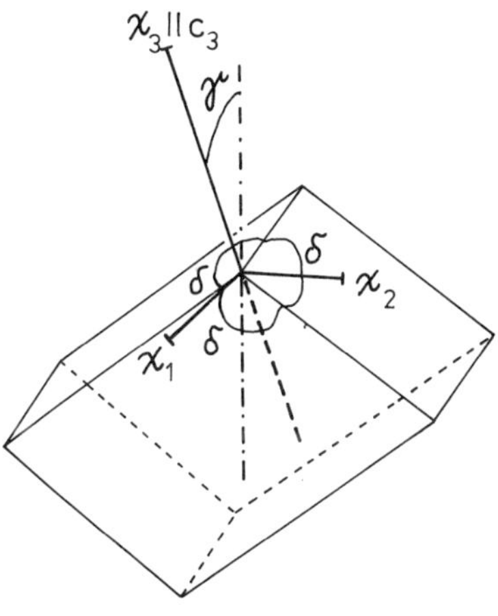

Figure 2.6. Principal axes of χ in a natural rhombohedron of calcite

In the simplest case a crystal plate can be suspended along a bisectrix of the angle δ. If we denote the angle between this direction and the threefold axis by γ, we have $\sin\gamma = (\sqrt{3}/3)\tan(\delta/2)$. Then the anisotropy measured for this suspension direction is in emu

$$\begin{aligned}\Delta\chi &= (\chi_1 - \chi_3)\sin^2\gamma \\ &= 2.21 \times 10^{-6}\ \text{cm}^3\,\text{mol}^{-1}.\end{aligned}$$

In addition to these two static measurements of the anisotropy, a dynamic measurement can be performed with the sample and suspension behaving as a torsional pendulum. The sample is suspended parallel to the axis of the principal susceptibility χ_2 in a homogeneous magnetic field H. When the sample is displaced by a small angle ε from equilibrium, the equation of motion has the form

$$I_2\ddot{\varepsilon} = -Ak(\chi_3 - \chi_1)\sin 2\varepsilon - k\varepsilon. \tag{2.3.11}$$

Here $\ddot{\varepsilon} = \mathrm{d}^2\varepsilon/\mathrm{d}t^2$ is the angular acceleration, with I_2 the moment of inertia about the axis of suspension; the two terms on the right-hand side are the torques arising from the magnetic field and the elasticity of the suspension respectively (cf. equations (2.3.5) and (2.3.7)) with A defined as previously. In the small-angle approximation $\sin 2\varepsilon \simeq 2\varepsilon$, equation (2.3.11) becomes

$$\ddot{\varepsilon} + [2A(\chi_3 - \chi_1) + 1]k\varepsilon/I_2 = 0. \tag{2.3.12}$$

Then the frequency of torsional oscillation in the magnetic field H is given by

$$\omega_{\mathrm{H}}^2 = [2A(\chi_3 - \chi_1) + 1]k/I_2, \tag{2.3.13}$$

where H determines A. In particular, with the magnetic field switched off we have $A = 0$ and the frequency of oscillation becomes

$$\omega_0^2 = k/I_2. \tag{2.3.14}$$

Combining equations (2.3.13) and (2.3.14) yields

$$\begin{aligned}2A(\chi_3 - \chi_1) &= \omega_{\mathrm{H}}^2/\omega_0^2 - 1 \\ &= T_0^2/T_{\mathrm{H}}^2 - 1\end{aligned} \tag{2.3.15}$$

where T_0 and T_{H} are the periods of oscillation corresponding to ω_0 and ω_{H}.

Thus measurement of the period or frequency of oscillation with and without the magnetic field allows the anisotropy $\chi_3 - \chi_1$ to be determined. The quantity A still depends on the torsional modulus k, which is conveniently obtained from measurements of the period T_{r} or frequency ω_{r} of oscillation of a reference body of known moment of inertia I_{r} replacing the crystal, since $\omega_{\mathrm{r}}^2 = 4\pi^2/T_{\mathrm{r}}^2 = k/I_{\mathrm{r}}$. For example, a cylindrical glass rod of mass M and length L suspended about its middle has moment of inertia $ML^2/12$ and serves as a convenient reference body.

2.4 ORIENTED GAS MODEL

2.4.1 Internal Field

It can be seen from (2.1.5) that the magnetic induction inside a diamagnetic substance differs from that in vacuum by the small term $\mu_0\Psi\boldsymbol{H}$. This difference is caused by the presence of the secondary field, $H' = \Psi H$, generated by the induced molecular magnetic moments. An interesting insight into that problem was given by Pople [17] by means of a model for the so-called 'ring current'. Briefly, the model is as follows, cf. Figure 2.7.

Suppose that the magnetic field vector $\boldsymbol{H}$ is directed perpendicular to the plane of the benzene ring. Each of the six mobile π-electrons then executes a Larmor precession round the direction of $\boldsymbol{H}$ of angular frequency $\omega = \mu_0 eH/(2m)$ which is equivalent to a 'current flow' i_r; e and m denote the charge and mass of the electron, respectively. The circulation of the ring current generates the magnetic field H' whose lines inside the ring are opposite to the applied field H. The induced magnetic moment is equal to i_r times the area enclosed by the ring contour, i.e.

$$p^{(i)} = i_r S = (6e)(\omega/2\pi)(\pi a^2) = \tfrac{3}{2}\mu_0 e^2 a^2 H/m. \tag{2.4.1}$$

(The hexagonal ring contour was replaced by a circle of radius a.) We can see that the resulting magnetic field inside the ring is slightly lower than the applied magnetic field and outside is slightly higher. This effect allowed Pople to explain the result of NMR measurements of the proton resonance frequency: for benzene the resonance was observed at lower fields H than it was in ethylene. The chemical shift calculated for benzene based upon (2.4.1), $+1.7$ ppm, compares well with the experimental value, $+1.4$ ppm.

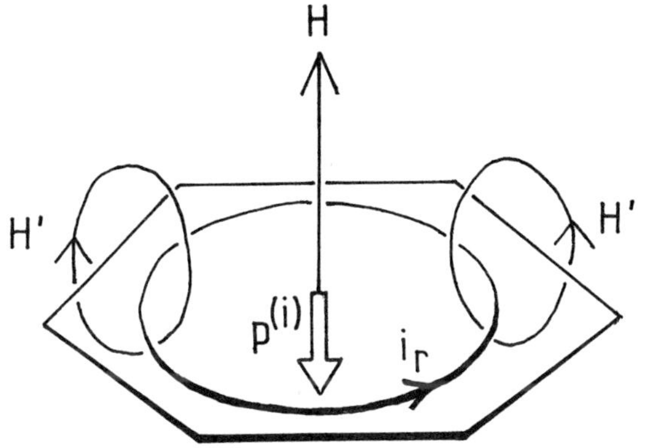

Figure 2.7. Secondary magnetic field of a benzene molecule induced by the ring current

Taking into account the result (2.4.1) we can now evaluate the magnitude of the secondary field strength, H'. For the benzene molecule, taken as an example, at a distance r from its centre we have

$$H' = \frac{p^{(i)}}{4\pi r^3} = \frac{1}{3}\frac{3\mu_0 e^2 a^2}{8\pi m r^3} H \qquad (2.4.2)$$

where the factor 1/3 comes from averaging over all directions in space [17]. Assuming $r = r(\mathrm{CC}) + r(\mathrm{CH}) = 0.25$ nm, and $a = r(\mathrm{CC}) = 0.14$ nm, we obtain from (2.4.2)

$$H'/H = 1.75 \times 10^{-6}$$

in close accordance to the absolute susceptibility values.

From these estimates we can judge that the additional magnetic field due to induced dipoles has at distances comparable with molecular diameter a value approximately a million times smaller than the applied field. Although the local fields in diamagnetics are negligible for bulk magnetic behaviour (which is our concern), they are of primary importance in NMR.

2.4.2 Systems of Coordinate Axes

The macroscopic molar susceptibility tensor of a crystal will be denoted by $\boldsymbol{\chi}$ while the microscopic molar susceptibility tensor will be denoted by $\boldsymbol{K}$. We then have

$$\mathrm{Tr}\,\boldsymbol{\chi} = \mathrm{Tr}\,\boldsymbol{K}. \qquad (2.4.3)$$

The contribution of a particular molecule will be referred to in a macroscopic system $x_1x_2x_3$ whose axes are parallel to the orthogonal crystallographic axes. In a crystallographic system possessing a symmetry not lower than that of the orthorhombic system the crystallographic axes a, b and c (or a_1, a_2, a_3) can be used. In the monoclinic system an orthogonalized set of axes a^*bc or abc^* is necessary, and the type to be applied is chosen in such a way that does not destroy the glide direction parallel to the a or c axis, respectively. If the glide direction is parallel to a cell diagonal or in the triclinic system, the type of orthogonalization may be chosen arbitrarily. In a properly orthogonalized system of axes all symmetry operations of the interchange group should be valid.

The choice of crystal axes is a matter of convention. A first proposition introduced by Krishnan [13] was modified by Lasheen [18]; the most widespread is as follows.

The principal axes of $\boldsymbol{\chi}$ are denoted by $X_1X_2X_3$ but the notation for principal values is different depending on the crystallographic system.

(1) In crystals possessing a symmetry axis of order higher than two the ellipsoid of magnitude illustrating all second rank tensors must have a rotational symmetry with the rotation axis coinciding with the crystal symmetry

axis (Neumann's principle). Hence only two quantities are necessary to characterize the magnetic susceptibility ellipsoid: $\chi_\parallel$ and $\chi_\perp$, respectively parallel and perpendicular to the symmetry axis which is usually chosen parallel to X_3. The remaining two coordinate axes, X_1 and X_2, can have arbitrary orientations. As there are no symmetry restrictions for the values of $\chi_\parallel$, $\chi_\perp$, it is said that the susceptibility ellipsoid has two degrees of freedom.

(2) In orthorhombic crystals the three principal axes of the susceptibility ellipsoid must be parallel to the crystallographic *a*, *b* and *c* axes, respectively, so that they have a fixed orientation in space. The principal values, denoted by χ_a, χ_b and χ_c, correspond to the three degrees of freedom.

(3) In the monoclinic system the principal values are denoted by χ_1, χ_2 and χ_3. Actually, an orientation $X_2 \parallel b$ with X_1 and X_3 situated in the plane (010) is preferred (in older papers a setting $X_3 \parallel b$ with X_1 and X_2 in the plane (010) can also be met). The angle made between X_1 and the direction [100] is denoted by θ. Sometimes instead the angle ψ made between X_1 and [001] is used. These angles are measured from [100] or [001], respectively, and are taken as positive when situated inside the monoclinic angle β and negative outside. An example of orientation with ψ negative is shown in Figure 2.8. The susceptibility ellipsoid has in this system four degrees of freedom: the magnitude of the three principal values and one angle of orientation.

(4) In the triclinic system there are no restrictions imposed by the symmetry either on the principal values or on the orientation of the principal axes. As a whole we have the maximum number of six degrees of freedom for the susceptibility ellipsoid.

In contrast to the crystallographic frame, a proper choice of the microscopic system of coordinate axes is a rather delicate problem. Usually the elements of $\boldsymbol{K}$ are expressed in the system of symmetry axes *LMN* of the *free*

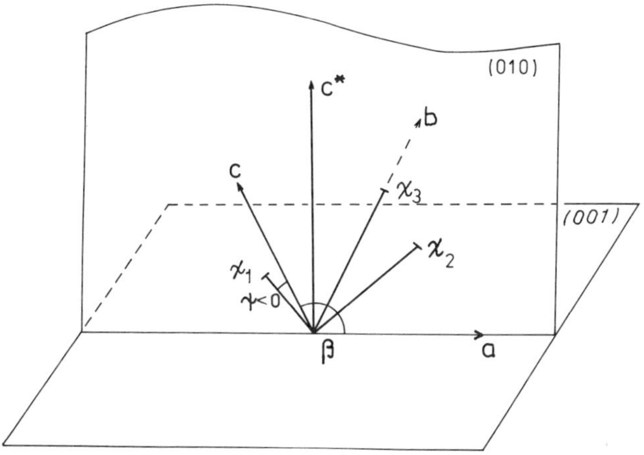

Figure 2.8. An example of the sequence of the principal diamagnetic and crystallographic axes in a monoclinic crystal

molecule; N is the plane normal (for planar molecules), and axes L, M are situated in molecular plane. Because the energy of interatomic interactions in a molecular crystal is small (not to be confused with interactions between magnetic dipoles) the choice of an axis system bound to a free molecule seems to be justified. Its orientation with respect to the orthogonalized crystallographic system is then given by the matrix $\mathbf{c}(r)$, $r = 1, 2, \ldots Z$, which was defined in Section 1.6. If, however, the deformation of the molecule as compared with its conformation in the free state cannot be neglected, a more general system $u_1u_2u_3$ should be defined. Its choice is determined by the symmetry of the site group; in C_1 or C_i point groups $u_1u_2u_3$ has an arbitrary orientation and in this case $\mathbf{K}$ contains six non-zero elements. Increasing symmetry of the site requires an increasing degree of correlation to be made between the axes u_i and the symmetry operations of the site group: certain axes must become parallel to the symmetry axes or perpendicular to symmetry planes. Simultaneously, symmetry reduces the number of non-zero components of $\mathbf{K}$ which must be invariant under all operations of the site group. In this case $\mathbf{c}$ is usually an unknown quantity. It is also not known when magnetic properties are examined of a crystalline polymorph whose structure has so far not been investigated. In such a case it is advisable to express the c_{ik} elements as functions of the three Euler angles describing the angular orientation of the $u_1u_2u_3$ system of axes. These functions are listed in many textbooks describing the rotational motion of a rigid body. If we are able to gain a knowledge of molecular susceptibilities in some other way, for example to calculate them from atomic increments or take their values from another polymorph whose magnetic properties are known, then we can find the approximate orientation of $u_1u_2u_3$ axes. The details of this 'reciprocal' problem are analysed in [19] and will not be considered here.

2.4.3 Susceptibility of the Unit Cell

The oriented gas model in diamagnetism is, in principle, a rule for averaging the molecular susceptibilities to obtain the crystal susceptibility when the interactions of the induced magnetic dipoles in neighbouring molecules are neglected. Because of the translational symmetry of the crystal the averaging can be restricted to the volume of one single unit cell which contains Z molecules (except for one class in the monoclinic and two classes in the trigonal crystallographic system Z is an even number).

To write the expression for the macroscopic susceptibility let us denote by $\mathbf{K}^{(s)}(LMN)$ the site invariant molecular tensor expressed in the local system of symmetry axes. $\mathbf{K}^{(s)}$ can be transformed to the orthogonalized crystallographic system by applying matrices $\mathbf{c}(r)$, $r = 1, 2, \ldots Z$. However, $\mathbf{c}(r)$ is obtained from $\mathbf{c}(1)$ according to (1.6.3) by means of symmetry operations $\mathbf{B}(r)$ of the exchange group. Therefore, for the contribution of the rth molecule we have

$$\boldsymbol{K}^{(c)}(r) = \boldsymbol{c}(r)^{\mathrm{T}}\boldsymbol{K}^{(s)}\boldsymbol{c}(r)$$
$$= \boldsymbol{B}(r)\boldsymbol{c}(1)^{\mathrm{T}}\boldsymbol{K}^{(s)}\boldsymbol{c}(1)\boldsymbol{B}(r)^{\mathrm{T}}.$$

Denoting by $\boldsymbol{K}^{(c)}$ the contribution of the molecule labelled by '1'

$$\boldsymbol{K}^{(c)} = \boldsymbol{c}(1)^{\mathrm{T}}\boldsymbol{K}^{(s)}\boldsymbol{c}(1) \tag{2.4.4}$$

we have

$$\boldsymbol{K}^{(c)}(r) = \boldsymbol{B}(r)\boldsymbol{K}^{(c)}\boldsymbol{B}(r)^{\mathrm{T}} \tag{2.4.5}$$

and

$$\boldsymbol{\chi} = Z^{-1} \sum_{r=1}^{Z} \boldsymbol{B}(r)\boldsymbol{K}^{(c)}\boldsymbol{B}(r)^{\mathrm{T}}. \tag{2.4.6}$$

Equation (2.4.6) gives the crystal susceptibility expressed as an average of the contributions of all Z molecules contained in the unit cell. Occasionally crystals are encountered in which the structure consists of crystallographically independent sublattices, an example being tetracene, and then the sum in equation (2.4.6) breaks up into separate sums for each independent sublattice.

Owing to the symmetry relations, $\boldsymbol{K}^{(c)}$ for a given crystal needs to be calculated just once; its components can be written as

$$K^{(c)}_{\alpha\beta} = c^{(1)}_{\alpha A} K_{AB} c^{(1)}_{B\beta} \tag{2.4.7}$$

where repeated Greek or capital Roman subscripts are understood to be summed over the values 1, 2 and 3 (Einstein convention). Note how the use of different types of letter for crystal and molecular axes helps to avoid error in writing (2.4.7) and similar equations when repeated subscripts are put adjacent; there is no need to specify whether $\boldsymbol{c}$ or $\boldsymbol{c}^{\mathrm{T}}$ is the first factor.

We may also require to relate the components of $\boldsymbol{\chi}$ in the crystal axis system $\boldsymbol{a}_\alpha$ to the principal components in the principal axis system X_i. If the matrix $\boldsymbol{g}$ describes the position of the principal axes such that its components are

$$g_{i\alpha} = X_i \cdot a_\alpha \tag{2.4.8}$$

then we have

$$\boldsymbol{\chi} = \boldsymbol{g}^{\mathrm{T}}\boldsymbol{\chi}^{(d)}\boldsymbol{g} \tag{2.4.9}$$

Here $\boldsymbol{\chi}^{(d)}$ is the diagonal matrix of the principal components χ_i, so that

$$\chi_{\alpha\beta} = g_{\alpha i}\chi_i g_{i\beta}. \tag{2.4.10}$$

Thus we can summarize the relation between principal, crystal and molecular susceptibilities from equations (2.4.6) and (2.4.9) as

$$\boldsymbol{g}^{\mathrm{T}} \cdot \boldsymbol{\chi}^{(d)} \cdot \boldsymbol{g} = \boldsymbol{\chi}$$
$$= Z^{-1} \sum_{r=1}^{Z} \boldsymbol{B}(r)\boldsymbol{K}^{(c)}\boldsymbol{B}(r)^{\mathrm{T}}. \tag{2.4.11}$$

The linear equations (2.4.11) may not always be sufficient in number to allow all components of $\boldsymbol{K}$ to be determined. In a triclinic crystal, $\boldsymbol{\chi}$ is specified by six quantities and the site symmetry is at most a centre of inversion so that $\boldsymbol{K}$ is also specified by six quantities. Then all the components of $\boldsymbol{K}$ can be deduced from those of $\boldsymbol{\chi}$. However, in crystals of higher symmetry, $\boldsymbol{\chi}$ is specified by four or fewer quantities while often the number of non-zero K_{ij} elements is still six because the site group symmetry is lower than that of the unit cell group or interchange group. As a rule, nature prefers to arrange unsymmetrical elements to construct more symmetrical structures. In such cases the components of $\boldsymbol{K}$ cannot be determined from those of $\boldsymbol{\chi}$ without further assumptions, for example treating as negligible any deviations of the site symmetry from the free molecule symmetry. Certain problems will be explained in two examples presented in the next section.

2.4.4 Examples: Benzene and Hexachlorobenzene

We now present detailed analyses of the crystal susceptibility data for these two substances to show how the molecular response can be obtained. Such analyses are possible only when sufficient magnetic and structural data are available, namely the full crystal susceptibility (to considerable accuracy), the atomic positions, and the space group, site group and interchange group symmetries.

(1) As already mentioned in Section 1.4, the *benzene* structure has centrosymmetric molecules at centrosymmetric sites. In this case the site group symmetry leaves all six elements of $\boldsymbol{K}^{(s)}$ unchanged. The unit cell of the *Pbca* orthorhombic crystal structure contains four molecules, the interchange operations being

$$\boldsymbol{B}(1)=\begin{pmatrix}1&0&0\\0&1&0\\0&0&1\end{pmatrix}\qquad \boldsymbol{B}(2)=\begin{pmatrix}1&0&0\\0&-1&0\\0&0&-1\end{pmatrix}$$
$$\boldsymbol{B}(3)=\begin{pmatrix}-1&0&0\\0&1&0\\0&0&-1\end{pmatrix}\qquad \boldsymbol{B}(4)=\begin{pmatrix}-1&0&0\\0&-1&0\\0&0&1\end{pmatrix}. \tag{2.4.12}$$

If the elements of $\boldsymbol{K}^{(c)}$ for molecule 1 expressed in the crystal axes (as defined in equation (2.4.4)) are symbolized by plus signs, then the four tensors $\boldsymbol{B}(r)\boldsymbol{K}^{(c)}\boldsymbol{B}(r)^{\mathrm{T}}$ contributing to $\boldsymbol{\chi}$ according to equation (2.4.6) can be symbolized by

$$\boldsymbol{K}^{(c)}(1)\approx\begin{pmatrix}+&+&+\\+&+&+\\+&+&+\end{pmatrix}\qquad \boldsymbol{K}^{(c)}(2)\approx\begin{pmatrix}+&-&-\\-&+&+\\-&+&+\end{pmatrix}$$
$$\boldsymbol{K}^{(c)}(3)\approx\begin{pmatrix}+&-&+\\-&+&-\\+&-&+\end{pmatrix}\qquad \boldsymbol{K}^{(c)}(4)\approx\begin{pmatrix}+&+&-\\+&+&-\\-&-&+\end{pmatrix}. \tag{2.4.13}$$

Then upon addition the resulting tensor $\boldsymbol{\chi}$ is obtained in diagonal form

$$\boldsymbol{\chi} \approx \begin{pmatrix} + & 0 & 0 \\ 0 & + & 0 \\ 0 & 0 & + \end{pmatrix}. \tag{2.4.14}$$

Thus we are left with only three equations that relate the crystal and molecular susceptibilities; in this case the crystal and principal axes coincide, so that $\boldsymbol{g} = \boldsymbol{1}$ in equation (2.4.11). The relevant equations are, from (2.4.6) and (2.4.7) with $K_{AB} = K_{BA}$,

$$\chi_a = c_{11}^2 K_{11} + c_{21}^2 K_{22} + c_{31}^2 K_{33} + 2c_{11}c_{21}K_{12} + 2c_{11}c_{31}K_{13} + 2c_{21}c_{31}K_{23} \tag{2.4.15}$$

$$\chi_b = c_{12}^2 K_{11} + c_{22}^2 K_{22} + c_{32}^2 K_{33} + 2c_{12}c_{22}K_{12} + 2c_{12}c_{32}K_{13} + 2c_{22}c_{32}K_{23} \tag{2.4.16}$$

$$\chi_c = c_{13}^2 K_{11} + c_{23}^2 K_{22} + c_{33}^2 K_{33} + 2c_{13}c_{23}K_{12} + 2c_{13}c_{33}K_{13} + 2c_{23}c_{33}K_{23} \tag{2.4.17}$$

However, these equations do not have a unique solution unless further conditions are imposed.

As X-ray data show, the normal to the benzene ring in the crystal is reasonably close to the hexagonal axis of the free molecule. The assumption that the molecule retains its hexagonal symmetry in the crystal reduces all the off-diagonal elements of $\boldsymbol{K}^{(c)}$ to zero and makes $K_{11} = K_{22}$. With this simplification, using the direction cosines $\boldsymbol{c}(1)$ and the principal susceptibilities given in Section 2.5.1, the solutions are

$$\boldsymbol{K}_{\text{emu}} = \begin{pmatrix} -34.9 & 0 & 0 \\ 0 & -34.9 & 0 \\ 0 & 0 & -94.6 \end{pmatrix} \times 10^{-6}\ \text{cm}^3\,\text{mol}^{-1}.$$

Alternatively, $\boldsymbol{K}_{\text{SI}}$ is given by the same matrix $\times 4\pi \times 10^{-6}\ \text{m}^3\,\text{mol}^{-1}$.

(2) *Hexachlorobenzene* crystallizes in the monoclinic $P2_1/c$ space group with $Z = 2$ molecules in the primitive unit cell; the unique axis is $b \parallel 2_1$. As in benzene, the molecules lie at centrosymmetric sites. The site group comprises the two elements $\{E\,|\,000\}$ and $\{C_i\,|\,000\}$ and the interchange group the two elements $\{E\,|\,000\}$ and $\{C_{2y}\,|\,0\,\frac{1}{2}\,\frac{1}{2}\}$. (An alternative interchange group with σ_y replacing C_{2y} is discarded because it does not preserve the handedness of axes, as discussed in Section 1.4 in connection with the *Pbca* space group.) The interchange point group operations are then represented by the matrices

$$\boldsymbol{B}(1) = \begin{pmatrix} 1 & 0 & 0 \\ 0 & 1 & 0 \\ 0 & 0 & 1 \end{pmatrix}, \qquad \boldsymbol{B}(2) = \begin{pmatrix} -1 & 0 & 0 \\ 0 & 1 & 0 \\ 0 & 0 & -1 \end{pmatrix}. \tag{2.4.18}$$

This situation is better than in benzene because $\boldsymbol{\chi}$ is specified by four independent non-zero elements rather than three, but there are still six unknown quantities required to specify the molecular susceptibility $\boldsymbol{K}$.

Thus we again need to increase the effective symmetry of the molecule in the crystal. Assuming that the molecule has an effective sixfold axis of symmetry would overdetermine the elements of $\boldsymbol{K}$. Instead we observe that the peripheral chlorine atoms are bulky enough to lead to some overcrowding. They are therefore liable to be displaced from the molecular plane, most probably alternately above and below it, although the X-ray structural determination shows that such displacements are small. The safest and simplest way to ascribe an increased symmetry to the molecule is then to assume a plane of symmetry perpendicular to the mean molecular plane and passing through opposite pairs of carbon and chlorine atoms, as shown in Figure 2.9.

In the L, M and N system of molecular axes appropriate to a planar molecule, the plane of symmetry reduces $\boldsymbol{K}$ to the form

$$\boldsymbol{K} = \begin{pmatrix} K_{LL} & 0 & K_{LN} \\ 0 & K_{MM} & 0 \\ K_{LN} & 0 & K_{NN} \end{pmatrix}. \tag{2.4.19}$$

This leads to the set of equations

$$\chi_1 \cos^2\theta + \chi_3 \sin^2\theta = c_{L1}^2 K_{LL} + c_{M1}^2 K_{MM} + c_{N1}^2 K_{NN} + 2c_{L1}c_{N1}K_{LN} \tag{2.4.20}$$

$$\chi_2 = c_{L2}^2 K_{LL} + c_{M2}^2 K_{MM} + c_{N2}^2 K_{NN} + 2c_{L2}c_{N2}K_{LN} \tag{2.4.21}$$

$$\chi_1 \sin^2\theta + \chi_3 \cos^2\theta = c_{L3}^2 K_{LL} + c_{M3}^2 K_{MM} + c_{N3}^2 K_{NN} + 2c_{L3}c_{N3}K_{LN} \tag{2.4.22}$$

$$(\chi_1 - \chi_3)\sin\theta\cos\theta = c_{L1}c_{L3}K_{LL} + c_{M1}c_{M3}K_{MM} + c_{N1}c_{N3}K_{NN} + 2c_{L1}c_{N3}K_{LN} \tag{2.4.23}$$

where the angle θ was explained previously.

Using the direction cosines $\boldsymbol{c}(1)$ and crystal susceptibility given in Section 2.5.12a, the solutions for the molecular susceptibilities are

$$\boldsymbol{K}_{\text{emu}} = \begin{pmatrix} -134.7 & 0 & +3.5 \\ 0 & -130.5 & 0 \\ +3.5 & 0 & -177.2 \end{pmatrix} \times 10^{-6}\ \text{cm}^3\,\text{mol}^{-1}.$$

We see that K_{LN} is non-zero but small compared with the diagonal elements. This indicates that the principal axes 1, 2 and 3 of the molecular tensor differ slightly from the molecular axes L, M and N. To diagonalize $\boldsymbol{K}$ it is necessary to rotate L and N about $M \equiv 2$ by the small angle ϕ, which satisfies

$$(K_{LL} - K_{NN})\sin\phi\cos\phi = K_{LN}(\cos^2\phi - \sin^2\phi) \tag{2.4.24}$$

or

$$\tan 2\phi = 2K_{LN}/(K_{LL} - K_{NN}). \tag{2.4.25}$$

Then we find $\phi = +4.7°$, the principal components of $\boldsymbol{K}$ being -135.6, -130.5 and $-176.4 \times 10^{-6}\ \text{cm}^3\,\text{mol}^{-1}$. However, as ϕ is small, its precise value is very sensitive to small variations in the input data. For example, using

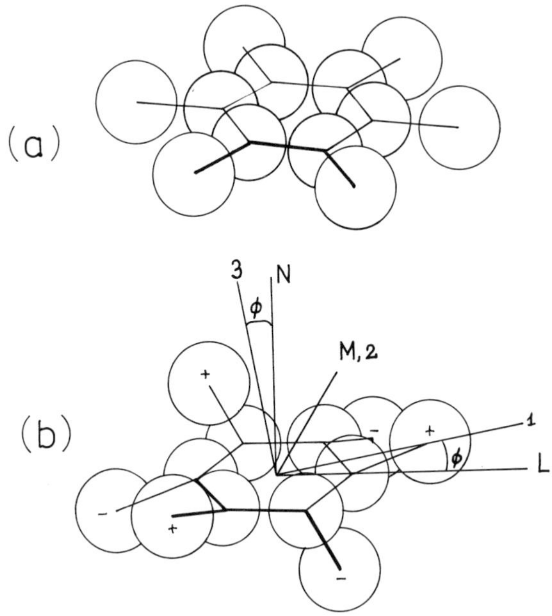

Figure 2.9. The molecule of hexachlorobenzene: (a) all atoms in one plane, (b) chlorine atoms displaced alternately with respect to the mean plane of carbon atoms

other susceptibility data for hexachlorobenzene given in Section 2.5.12b (but with a different choice of unit cell) we obtain $\phi = +6.8^\circ$ and principal components -137.9, -128.9 and $-175.6 \times 10^{-6}\ \mathrm{cm^3\,mol^{-1}}$.

These two examples illustrate the correlation between the crystal and molecular symmetries and the number of elements of $\boldsymbol{K}$ that can be deduced from $\boldsymbol{\chi}$. As we have seen, in crystals with higher symmetry the symmetry of the molecule has to be 'adjusted' to obtain a solution. This can be done using the lowest-symmetry site group sufficient to reduce the number of unknowns to the number of equations. This leads to the most reliable set of molecular susceptibilities and may sometimes give additional insights into features such as the configuration of the molecule.

2.5 TABLE OF CRYSTAL AND MOLECULAR PROPERTIES

This section comprises a collection of crystal and molecular susceptibilities of organic compounds, together with the crystallographic information used in deducing the molecular properties. All susceptibilities are given as $\chi_{\mathrm{emu}}/10^{-6}\ \mathrm{cm^3\,mol^{-1}}$ or $K_{\mathrm{emu}}/10^{-6}\ \mathrm{cm^3\,mol^{-1}}$, corresponding to $\chi_{\mathrm{SI}}/4\pi \times 10^{-12}\ \mathrm{m^3\,mol^{-1}}$, or $K_{\mathrm{SI}}/4\pi \times 10^{-12}\ \mathrm{m^3\,mol^{-1}}$. Averaged values, as measured for powders, are denoted by angle brackets. The notation for the crystal and molecular axes and orientation of principal axes follows that explained in Section 2.4.2.

2.5.1 Benzene, C_6H_6

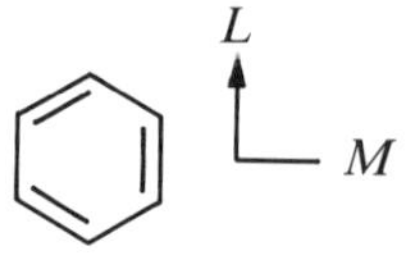

(1) Crystal structure [20]
Orthorhombic
$a = 7.460$, $b = 9.666$, $c = 7.033$ Å at 270 K
Space group $Pbca$, site group $\bar{1}$, $Z = 4$.

(2) Molecular geometry [20]
The molecule is planar within experimental error. The molecule has D_{6h} symmetry in the free state and C_i in the crystal, but the deviations from the free symmetry are small. According to other experimental results (for example, UV spectroscopy) the molecular symmetry in the crystal ranges from C_{2h} to D_{6h} [21].

(3) Crystal susceptibilities

	$\langle\chi\rangle$	χ_a	χ_b	χ_c	T/K
[23]	−54.8	−65.2	−37.9	−61.3	261
[22]	−54.8	−65.3	−37.6	−61.35	270

(4) Orientation of molecular LMN axes [24]

	a	b	c
L	−0.276	0.961	−0.029
M	−0.649	−0.163	0.743
N	0.709	0.224	0.668

(5) Molecular susceptibilities

	K_L	K_M	K_N
[22]	−34.9	−34.9	−94.6
[24]	−34.8	−32.2	−97.4

2.5.2 *p*-Benzoquinone, $C_6H_4O_2$

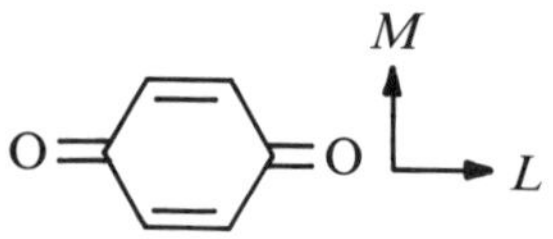

(1) Crystal structure [25]
Monoclinic
$a = 7.055$, $b = 6.795$, $c = 5.767$ Å, $\beta = 101.47°$
Space group $P2_1/a$, site group $\bar{1}$, $Z = 2$.

(2) Molecular geometry [25]
The molecule is planar within experimental error (largest deviations from the mean molecular plane are 0.007 Å). The molecule has symmetry *mmm* in the free state and $\bar{1}$ in the crystal.
(3) Crystal susceptibilities

	$\langle\chi\rangle$	χ_1	χ_2	χ_3	ψ	
[12]	−40.0	−27.1	−67.1	−25.9	+31.2°	(obs)
[19]	−38.4	−25.7	−65.3	−24.3	+30.7°	(obs)

(4) Orientation of molecular *LMN* axes [25]

	a^*	b	c
L	0.3120	0.8178	0.4835
M	0.4207	−0.5740	0.7025
N	0.8522	−0.0153	−0.5229

(5) Molecular susceptibilities

	K_L	K_M	K_N
[26]	−24.3	−28.7	−67.1
[19]	−23.0	−27.0	−65.2

	K_{11}	K_{22}	K_{33}	K_{13}	
[24]	−24.8	−28.2	−67.1	−0.4	(χ_i from [12])
[24]	−23.1	−27.0	−65.3	−1.0	(χ_i from [19])

2.5.3 Tetrachloro-*p*-benzoquinone, $C_6Cl_4O_2$

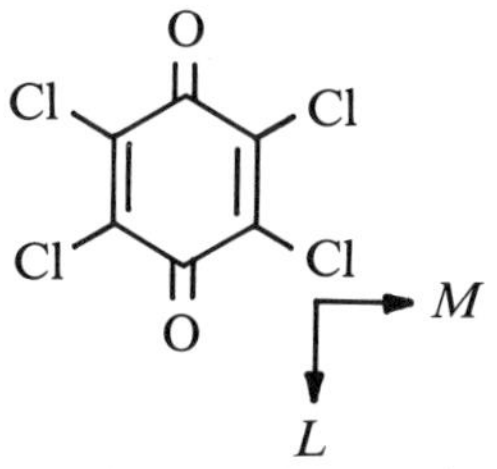

(1) Crystal structure [27]
Monoclinic
$a = 8.708$, $b = 5.755$, $c = 8.603$ Å, $\beta = 105.85°$
Space group $P2_1/a$, site group $\bar{1}$, $Z = 2$.
(2) Molecular geometry [27]
The quinone ring is planar but the deviations of the substituents from this plane are significant. They average +0.05 Å, which corresponds to a bending angle of 1.5° for the C—Cl bond, and 2.1° for the C=O bond.
(3) Crystal susceptibilities

	$\langle\chi\rangle$	χ_1	χ_2	χ_3	θ
[28]	—	−93.9	−116.2	−96.2	+90°
[19]	−107.12	−98.52	−121.72	−101.12	+90°

(4) Orientation of molecular *LMN* axes [27]

	a^*	b	c
L	0.5390	0.8306	−0.1399
M	0.2604	−0.0064	0.9655
N	−0.8011	0.5569	0.2197

(5) Molecular susceptibilities

	K_L	K_M	K_N
[19]	−84.4	−98.5	−138.5

2.5.4 Tetrachlorohydroquinone, $C_6Cl_4(OH)_2$

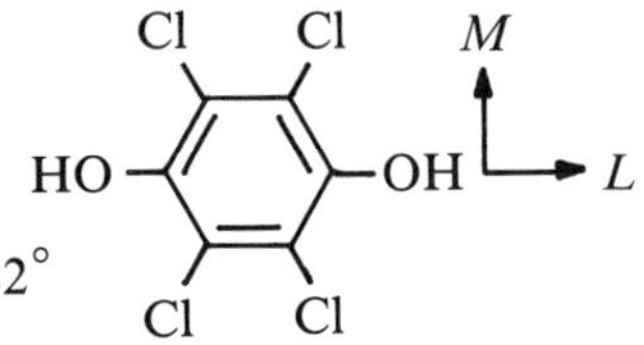

(1) Crystal structure [29]
Monoclinic
$a = 8.214$, $b = 4.843$, $c = 12.441$ Å, $\beta = 123.82°$
Space group $P2_1/c$, site group $\bar{1}$, $Z = 2$.
(2) Molecular geometry [29]
The molecule is planar within experimental error.
(3) Crystal susceptibilities

	$\langle\chi\rangle$	χ_1	χ_2	χ_3	θ	
[19]	−120.7	−103.5	−129.2	−129.4	+29.9°	(obs)

(4) Orientation of molecular *LMN* axes [19]

	a^*	b	c
L	0.982	−0.108	0.155
M	−0.201	−0.694	0.691
N	−0.035	0.710	0.703

(5) Molecular susceptibilities

	K_L	K_M	K_N
[19]	−103.0	−114.3	−144.9

2.5.5 *p*-Dichlorobenzene, $C_6H_4Cl_2$

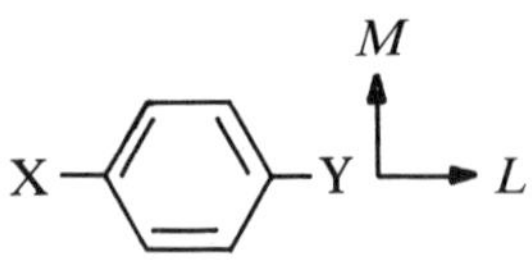

2.5.6 *p*-Chlorobromobenzene, C_6H_4ClBr

2.5.7 *p*-Dibromobenzene, $C_6H_4Br_2$

(1) Crystal structures [30, 31, 32]
The structures of these three compounds are monoclinic and isomorphous.
Cl, Cl: $a = 14.80$, $b = 5.78$, $c = 3.99$ Å, $\beta = 113^\circ$
Cl, Br: $a = 15.20$, $b = 5.86$, $c = 4.11$ Å, $\beta = 113.2^\circ$
Br, Br: $a = 15.36$, $b = 5.75$, $c = 4.10$ Å, $\beta = 112.63^\circ$
In all three cases the space group is $P2_1/a$, site group $\bar{1}$, $Z = 2$.

(2) Molecular geometry [30]
The molecules are planar, and those symmetrically substituted have a centre of symmetry. The carbon rings are regular hexagons within the limits of experimental error.

(3) Crystal susceptibilities

		$\langle\chi\rangle$	χ_1	χ_2	χ_3	ψ	
Cl, Cl	[12]	−85.4	−70.0	−106.2	−79.9	+86.9°	
	[19]	−82.93	−67.36	−103.76	−77.66	+87.4°	(obs)
Cl, Br	[19]	−92.16	−77.3	−112.3	−86.9	+87.2°	(obs)
Br, Br	[12]	−100.1	−86.3	−118.5	−95.4	+87.0°	
	[19]	−101.4	−87.0	−120.7	−96.4	+87.1°	(obs)

(4) Orientation of molecular *LMN* axes [19]

	Cl, Cl			Br, Br		
	a	*b*	c^*	*a*	*b*	c^*
L	0.7898	−0.6116	0.0474	0.8092	−0.5871	0.0213
M	0.4417	0.6206	0.6478	0.4752	0.6328	0.6112
N	0.4255	0.4909	−0.7602	0.3527	0.4993	−0.7915

Cl, Br (mean orientation)

	a	*b*	c^*
L	0.7995	−0.5994	0.0131
M	0.4585	0.6267	0.6295
N	0.3891	0.4951	−0.7759

(5) Molecular susceptibilities

		K_L	K_M	K_N
[19]	Cl, Cl	−78.3	−50.3	−120.2
[19]	Cl, Br	−87.6	−59.9	−129.0
[19]	Br, Br	−97.1	−70.5	−136.7

2.5.8 1,4-Dimethoxybenzene, $C_6H_4(OCH_3)_2$

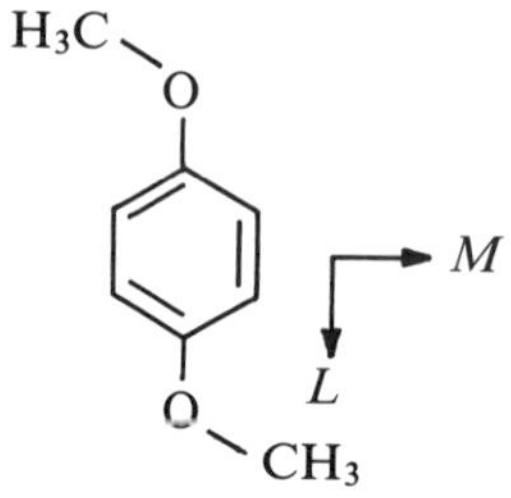

(1) Crystal structure [33]
Orthorhombic
$a = 7.29, b = 6.30, c = 16.55$ Å
Space group *Pbca*, $Z = 4$.
(2) Molecular geometry [33]
Planar carbon ring with a centre of symmetry.
(3) Crystal susceptibilities

	$\langle\chi\rangle$	χ_a	χ_b	χ_c
[34]	− 86.65	− 104.5 ± 0.2	− 86.3 ± 0.3	− 69.2 ± 0.3

(4) Orientation of molecular *LMN* axes [33]

	a	*b*	*c*
L	0.0290	0.3635	0.9313
M	0.5499	− 0.7836	0.2887
N	0.8348	0.5038	− 0.2228

(5) Molecular susceptibilities

	K_L	K_M	K_N
[34]	− 65.6 ± 0.4	− 78.6 ± 0.7	− 115.8 ± 0.5

2.5.9 *m*-Dinitrobenzene, $C_6H_4(NO_2)_2$

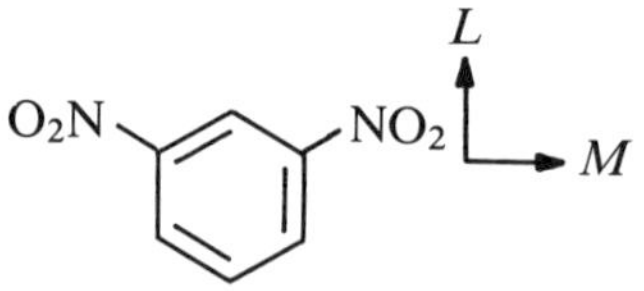

(1) Crystal structure [35]
Orthorhombic
$a = 13.20, b = 13.97, c = 3.80$ Å
Space group $Pbn2_1$, $Z = 4$.
(2) Molecular geometry [35]
The carbon and nitrogen atoms are situated in one plane but the $-NO_2$ groups are twisted from this plane by angles 11.8° and 9.6°.
(3) Crystal susceptibilities

	$\langle\chi\rangle$	χ_a	χ_b	χ_c
[28]	− 68.9	− 43.6	− 57.3	− 105.8
[34]	− 70.53	− 45.1 ± 2.3	− 58.9 ± 2.4	− 107.5 ± 4.6

(4) Orientation of molecular *LMN* axes [34]

	a	*b*	*c*
L	0.5786	−0.7238	0.3744
M	0.8109	0.5596	−0.1713
N	0.0871	−0.4048	−0.9103

(5) Molecular susceptibilities

	K_L	K_M	K_N
[34]	−50.0 ± 6.9	−41.7 ± 2.1	−119.8 ± 6.7
[24]	−48.3	−40.3	−118.1

2.5.10 *α-p*-Nitrophenol, $C_6H_4(OH)NO_2$

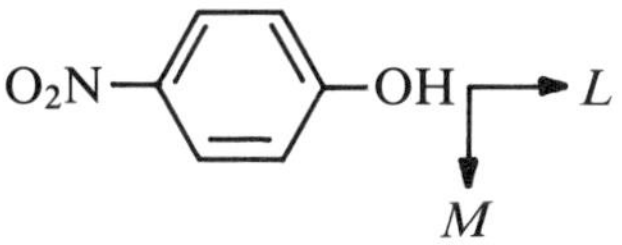

(1) Crystal structure [36]
Monoclinic
$a = 11.66, b = 8.78, c = 6.098$ Å, $\beta = 107.53°$ (90 K)
Space group $P2_1/n$, $Z = 4$.
Molecules are joined by OH ... O 'head-to-tail' hydrogen bonds, the mean chain direction being approximately parallel to the crystallographic *c* axis.

(2) Molecular geometry [36]
The carbon ring is planar within ±0.004 Å; the plane of the nitro group makes an angle of 1.5° with the carbon ring.

(3) Crystal susceptibilities

	$\langle\chi\rangle$	χ_1	χ_2	χ_3	θ	
[37]	−65.66	−48.1	−82.2	−66.7	−40.0°	(obs)

(4) Orientation of *LMN* axes (carbon atoms only) [36], 90 K

	a	*b*	*c**
L	−0.8417	−0.4426	0.3094
M	0.0762	−0.6646	−0.7433
N	0.5346	−0.6020	0.5931

(5) Molecular susceptibilities

	K_L	K_M	K_N
[37]	−49.4	−44.6	−102.9

2.5.11 β-p-Nitrophenol, $C_6H_4(OH)NO_2$

(1) Crystal structure [36]
Monoclinic
$a = 15.403, b = 11.117, c = 3.785$ Å, $\beta = 107.10°$
Space group $P2_1/a$, $Z = 4$.
Molecules are joined by OH ... O 'head-to-tail' hydrogen bonds, the mean chain direction being approximately parallel to the crystallographic a axis.

(2) Molecular geometry [36]
The carbon ring is planar within ±0.002 Å; the plane of the nitro group makes an angle of 7.2° with the carbon ring.

(3) Crystal susceptibilities

	$\langle\chi\rangle$	χ_1	χ_2	χ_3	θ	
[37]	−65.66	−49.4	−97.2	−50.4	−5.2°	(calc)

(4) Orientation of molecular LMN axes (carbon atoms only) [36]

	a	b	c^*
L	0.920 83	0.388 22	0.036 89
M	−0.384 82	0.889 26	0.247 25
N	0.063 19	−0.241 87	0.968 25

(5) Molecular susceptibilities

	K_L	K_M	K_N
[37]	−49.9	−46.8	−100.3

2.5.12a Hexachlorobenzene (Data 1), C_6Cl_6

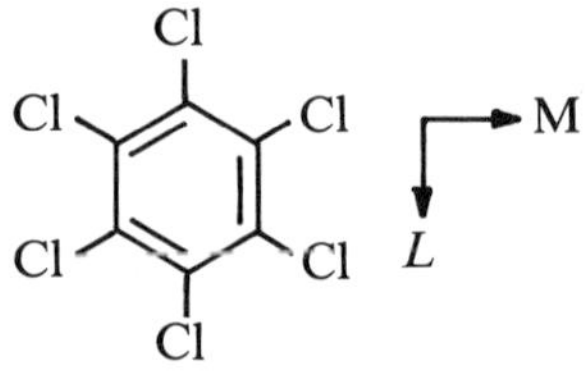

(1) Crystal structure [38]
Monoclinic
$a = 8.0476(8), b = 3.8363(5), c = 14.8208(29)$ Å, $\beta = 92.134(14)°$
Space group $P2_1/n$, $Z = 2$.

(2) Molecular geometry [38]
The carbon ring is nearly planar: the largest deviation from the best plane amounts to 8×10^{-4} Å. Three consecutive chlorine atoms deviate from this plane by 0.014, −0.020 and 0.015 Å. The molecular symmetry in the crystal is near to $6/mmm$.

(3) Crystal susceptibilities [39]

⟨χ⟩	χ_1	χ_2	χ_3	θ	
−147.5 [14]	−132.2	−137.9	−172.3	93.6°	(obs)

(4) Orientation of molecular *LMN* axes (carbon atoms only) [24]

		a	*b*	c^*
L	(∥ Cl1−Cl1′)	0.8952	0.3080	−0.3220
M		0.2511	0.2483	0.9356
N		0.3681	−0.9184	0.1449

(5) Molecular susceptibilities

	K_L	K_M	K_N
[24]	−130.88	−131.59	−179.93

	K_{11}	K_{22}	K_{33}	K_{13}	
[24]	−134.7	−130.5	−177.2	+3.5	(in *LMN*)

2.5.12b Hexachlorobenzene (Data 2), C_6Cl_6

(1) Crystal structure [40]
Monoclinic
$a = 8.08, b = 3.87, c = 16.65$ Å, $\beta = 117.0°$
Space group $P2_1/c$, $Z = 2$.
(2) Molecular geometry [40]
The molecule is a regular hexagon and planar.
(3) Crystal susceptibilities

	⟨χ⟩	χ_1	χ_2	χ_3	ψ
[12]	−145.6	−129.4	−136.2	−171.1	+52.6° (obs)
[34]	−147.5	−132.2 ± 0.4	−137.9 ± 0.4	−172.5 ± 0.6	+5.9 ± 7.3° (obs)

(4) Orientation of molecular *LMN* axes [19]

		a	*b*	c^*
L	(∥ Cl1−Cl1′)	0.9253	0.1988	0.3229
M		0.2590	0.2907	−0.9212
N		0.2691	−0.9375	−0.2202

(5) Molecular susceptibilities

	K_L	K_M	K_N
[34]	− 132.3 ± 0.3	− 132.2 ± 0.3	− 177.4 ± 0.4

2.5.13 Pentachlorophenol, $C_6Cl_5(OH)$

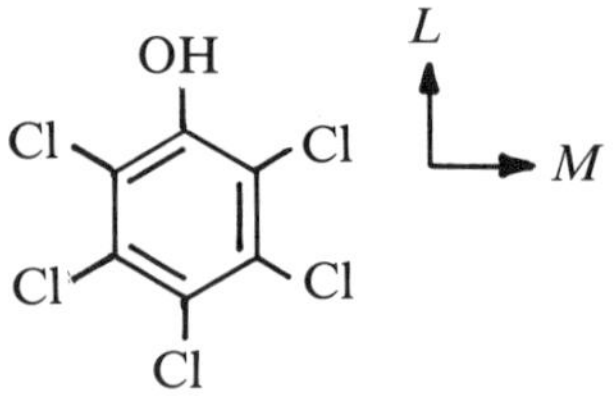

(1) Crystal structure [41]
Monoclinic
$a = 29.11, b = 4.930, c = 12.09$ Å, $\beta = 93.63°$
Space group $C2/c$, $Z = 8$.
The substance is dimorphic: at 63°C a phase transition occurs [42, 43]. The crystal data given refer to the low-temperature phase which is hydrogen bonded by bonds of the type OH ··· O.

(2) Molecular geometry [41]
The carbon ring is nearly planar and the deviations of chlorine atoms from the mean plane are small (compare hexachlorobenzene, 2.5.12a).

(3) Crystal susceptibilities [34]

$\langle\chi\rangle$	χ_1	χ_2	χ_3	ψ
− 141.5	− 125.4 ± 0.7	− 150.3 ± 0.7	− 148.9 ± 0.3	+ 81.4 ± 1.5° (obs)

(4) Orientation of molecular LMN axes [41]

	a^*	b	c
L	0.9814	0.0769	0.1758
M	0.1778	− 0.7094	− 0.6823
N	0.0651	0.7006	− 0.7114

(5) Molecular susceptibilities

	K_L	K_M	K_N
[34]	− 125.5 ± 0.6	− 125.3 ± 18.8	− 173.8 ± 18.9

2.5.14 Benzoic Acid (Dimer), $(C_7H_6O_2)_2$

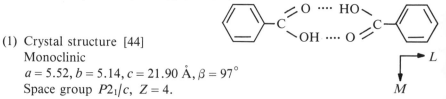

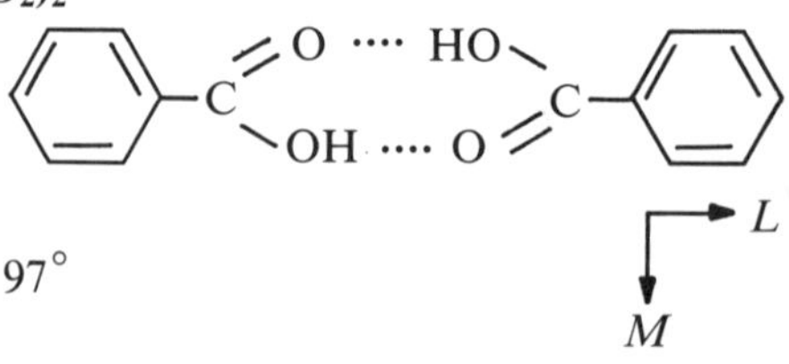

(1) Crystal structure [44]
Monoclinic
$a = 5.52, b = 5.14, c = 21.90$ Å, $\beta = 97°$
Space group $P2_1/c$, $Z = 4$.

(2) Molecular geometry [44]
The molecules are fully associated into dimers by means of two symmetrical OH ... O hydrogen bonds. Each dimer is planar within the limits of few hundredths of an ångstrom.

(3) Crystal susceptibilities [45]

$\langle\chi\rangle$		χ_1	χ_2	χ_3	ψ
−70.4	[46, 47]	−50.8	−82.7	−77.9	−41.7°

(4) Orientation of molecular *LMN* axes [24]

	a	b	c^*
L	0.2118	0.7189	0.6621
M	−0.8229	−0.2342	0.5176
N	0.5276	−0.6546	0.5420

(5) Molecular susceptibilities

	K_L	K_M	K_N
[24]	−54.9	−46.8	−109.6

	K_{11}	K_{22}	K_{33}	K_{13}
[24]	−59.4	−50.0	−101.9	+0.82

2.5.15 Anthranilic Acid, $C_6H_4NH_2COOH$

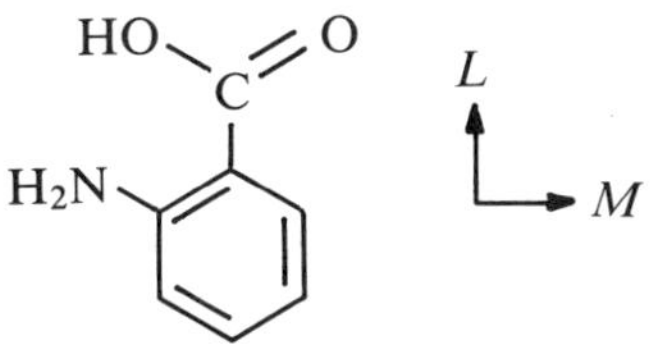

(1) Crystal structure [19]
Orthorhombic
$a = 12.83, b = 10.77, c = 9.28$ Å
Space group $Pcn2$, $Z = 8$ (the unit cell contains two independent sets of molecules).

(2) Molecular geometry [19]
The molecule is not planar: the carbon atoms of the benzene ring are alternately displaced by ±0.015 Å with respect to the mean ring plane. Molecules are associated into pairs with one of the two molecules forming a double ion ('zwitter-ion'). The angle made between the carboxylic group and each of the carbon rings in the pair is 6.85 and 2.3°.

(3) Crystal susceptibilities [19]

$\langle\chi\rangle$	χ_a	χ_b	χ_c
−79.0	−112.5	−59.3	−65.3

(4) Orientation of molecular *LMN* axes [19]

		a	*b*	*c*		*a*	*b*	*c*
A.	*L*	0.3109	−0.2934	0.9038	B.	−0.2897	0.3713	0.8823
	M	0.1865	0.9470	0.2624		0.2138	0.9295	−0.3014
	N	−0.9304	0.0837	0.3568		0.9356	−0.1045	0.3388

(5) Molecular susceptibilities

	K_L	K_M	K_N
[19]	−57.7	−58.8	−120.5

2.5.16 Acetanilide, $C_6H_5NHCOCH_3$

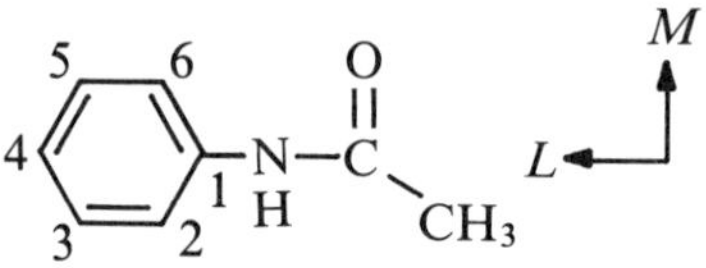

(1) Crystal structure [48]
Orthorhombic
$a = 19.640, b = 9.483, c = 7.979$ Å
Space group *Pbca*, $Z = 8$.

(2) Molecular geometry [48]
The carbon atoms are situated in two planes: that containing the benzene ring and that through the carbon atoms and oxygen forming the acetyl group. These planes make an angle of 37.9°. In the crystal molecules are present in the amide form (but not in the imide form).

(3) Crystal susceptibilities

	$\langle\chi\rangle$	χ_a	χ_b	χ_c
[19]	−72.2	−57.4	−66.4	−93.0

(4) Orientation of molecular *LMN* axes [19]

		a	*b*	*c*
L	(‖ C4–C1)	0.9289	−0.1404	0.3428
M	(‖ C3–C5)	0.3073	0.8211	−0.4811
N		0.2074	−0.5512	−0.8082

(5) Molecular susceptibilities

	K_L	K_M	K_N
[19]	−55.9	−44.3	−116.6

2.5.17 *p*-Nitroaniline, $C_6H_4(NO_2)NH_2$

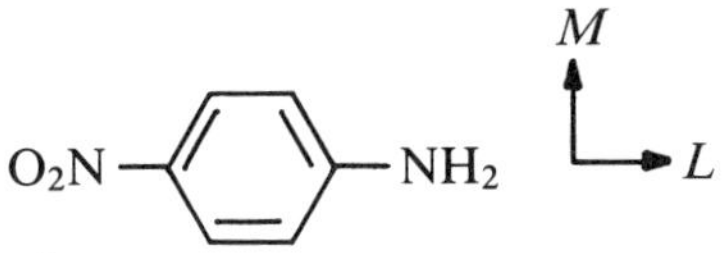

(1) Crystal structure [49]
Monoclinic
$a = 12.336, b = 6.07, c = 8.592$ Å, $\beta = 91.45°$
Space group $P2_1/n$, $Z = 4$.

(2) Molecular geometry [49]
The benzene ring is planar. The nitro group is twisted from that plane by 1.9°, and the amine group is twisted by 16°.

(3) Crystal susceptibilities

	$\langle\chi\rangle$	χ_1	χ_2	χ_3	θ
[19]	−66.6	−50.0	−94.8	−54.9	−47.0° (obs)
[50]	−66.28	−48.1 ± 1.4	−97.1 ± 2.8	−53.7 ± 1.4	−47.2° (obs)

(4) Orientation of molecular *LMN* axes [49]

	a^*	b	c
L	0.7501	−0.4334	−0.4994
M	0.0730	0.8030	−0.5915
N	0.6563	0.4077	0.6348

(5) Molecular susceptibilities

	K_L	K_M	K_N
[19]	−52.0	−43.0	−104.8
[50]	−50.1	−40.9	−107.8

2.5.18 Isatin, $C_8H_5O_2N$ (lactam of isatinic acid)

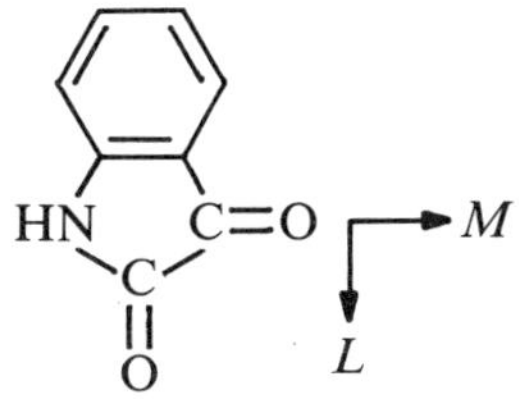

(1) Crystal structure [51]
Monoclinic
$a = 6.19, b = 14.46, c = 7.17$ Å, $\beta = 94.82°$
Space group $P2_1/c$, $Z = 4$.

(2) Molecular geometry [51]
The molecule is planar within the limits of experimental error.

(3) Crystal susceptibilities

	$\langle\chi\rangle$	χ_1	χ_2	χ_3	θ
[19]	−81.15	−57.45	−123.85	−62.15	+21.5°

(4) Orientation of molecular *LMN* axes [51]

	a	*b*	c^*
L	0.1814	−0.9815	0.0611
M	0.9095	0.1911	0.3694
N	0.3736	0.0123	−0.9261

(5) Molecular susceptibilities

	K_L	K_M	K_N
[19]	−62.0	−57.3	−124.2

2.5.19 Hydrogen Sodium Phthalate, $C_6H_4(COOH)(COONa)$, (NaHPh)

2.5.20 Hydrogen Potassium Phthalate, $C_6H_4(COOH)(COOK)$, (KHPh)

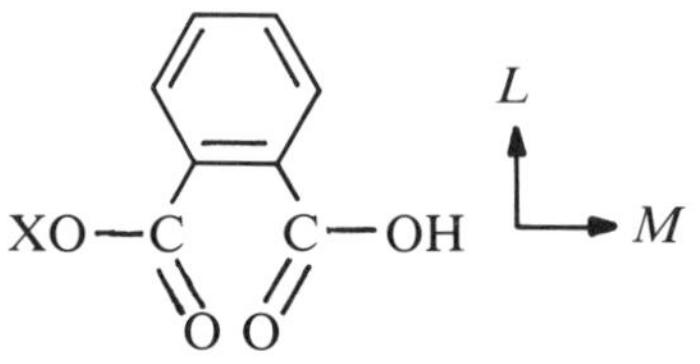

(1) Crystal structure [52]
The structure of the three monosubstituted phthalates, i.e. sodium, ammonium, and potassium hydrogen phthalate is orthorhombic. There are relations between unit-cell dimensions of the three salts but the structures are not isomorphous.

Salt	*a*	*b*	*c*	Space group	*Z*
NaHPh	6.76	9.31	26.42	*B2ab*	8
AHPh	6.40	10.23	26.14	*Pcab*	8
KHPh	6.47	9.61	13.26	$P2_12_12_1$	4

(2) Molecular geometry [52]
The carbon ring and the two carbonyl atoms form one plane; the planes of the two carboxylic groups are twisted by 21 and 65°, respectively. The benzene ring is not an exact hexagon because the C—C distances vary from 1.35 to 1.40 Å.

(3) Crystal susceptibilities [19]

	$\langle\chi\rangle$	χ_a	χ_b	χ_c
NaHPh	−89.9	−115.4	−79.1	−75.1
KHPh	−99.2	−124.95	−89.35	−83.25

(4) Orientation of molecular *LMN* axes (the same for NaHPh and KHPh) [52]

	a	*b*	*c*
L	0.2382	0.4578	−0.8565
M	0.4873	−0.8192	−0.3024
N	0.8368	0.3390	0.4300

(5) Molecular susceptibilities

		K_L	K_M	K_N
NaHPh	[19]	−59.1	−76.5	−134.1
KHPh	[19]	−66.4	−87.9	−143.3

2.5.21 Naphthalene, $C_{10}H_8$

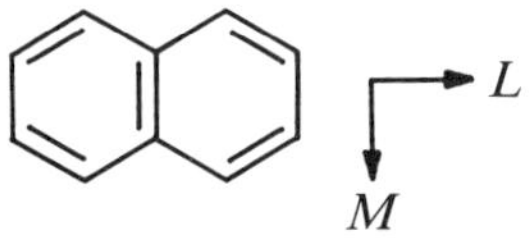

(1) Crystal structure [53]
Monoclinic
$a = 8.235, b = 6.003, c = 8.658$ Å, $\beta = 122.92°$
Space group $P2_1/a$, site group $\bar{1}$, $Z = 2$.

(2) Molecular geometry [53]
The molecule is planar; deviations of the carbon atoms from the mean molecular plane do not exceed 0.007 Å.

(3) Crystal susceptibilities

	$\langle\chi\rangle$	χ_1	χ_2	χ_3	ψ
[26]	−93.0	−56.0	−146.4	−76.6	+12.0°

(4) Orientation of molecular *LMN* axes [53]

	a	*b*	c^*
L	−0.4379	−0.2103	0.8741
M	−0.3207	−0.8718	−0.3704
N	0.8399	−0.4425	0.3143

(5) Molecular susceptibilities

	K_L	K_M	K_N
[26]	−56.1	−53.9	−169.0

	K_{11}	K_{22}	K_{33}	K_{13}
[24]	−56.14	−53.69	−169.16	−1.01

2.5.22 Biphenyl, $C_{12}H_{10}$

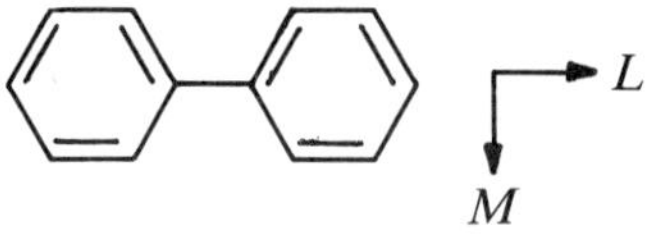

(1) Crystal structure [54, 55]
Monoclinic
$a = 8.12_4, b = 5.63_5, c = 9.15_3$ Å, $\beta = 95.1°$
Space group $P2_1/a$, $Z = 2$.

(2) Molecular geometry [54]
The whole molecule is planar in the crystal within the limits of experimental error but exhibits large-amplitude torsional oscillations about the bridging C—C bond [56]. The length of the bridging C—C bond indicates that the conjugation between the two benzene rings, if any, is very small.

(3) Crystal susceptibilities

	$\langle\chi\rangle$	χ_1	χ_2	χ_3	ψ
[11]	−102.9	−63.4	−146.5	−98.9	+20.1°
[19]	−104.4	−67.4	−144.9	−100.9	+22.4° (obs)

(4) Orientation of molecular *LMN* axes [19]

	a	b	c^*
L	0.2966	−0.0256	0.9545
M	0.5355	−0.8233	−0.1881
N	0.7928	0.5669	−0.2243

(5) Molecular susceptibilities

	K_L	K_M	K_N
[19]	−67.7	−61.7	−183.8

2.5.23 Acenaphthene, $C_{10}H_6(CH_2)_2$

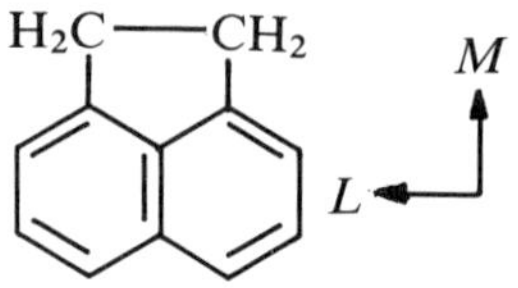

(1) Crystal structure [57]
Orthorhombic
$a = 8.290, b = 14.000, c = 7.225$ Å (15 °C)
Space group $Pcm2_1$, $Z = 4$ (the unit cell contains two symmetrically independent sets of two molecules).

(2) Molecular geometry [57]
The molecules are planar and have a symmetry plane which passes through the C—C bond common to the two benzene rings and the plane normal, *N*. The *L* axis of the two types of molecule is parallel to the crystallographic axis *b*.

(3) Crystal susceptibilities

	⟨χ⟩	χ_a	χ_b	χ_c
[11]	−111.8	−117.6	−72.1	−145.6
[19]	−109.3	−114.9	−72.0	−141.1

(4) Orientation of molecular *LMN* axes [57]

	a	*b*	*c*	*a*	*b*	*c*
L	0	1	0	0	1	0
M	1	0	0	0.4772	0	0.8788
N	0	0	1	0.8788	0	−0.4772

(5) Molecular susceptibilities

	K_L	K_M	K_N
[19]	−72.0	−70.5	−185.5

2.5.24 2-Naphthol (β-Naphthol), $C_{10}H_7(OH)$

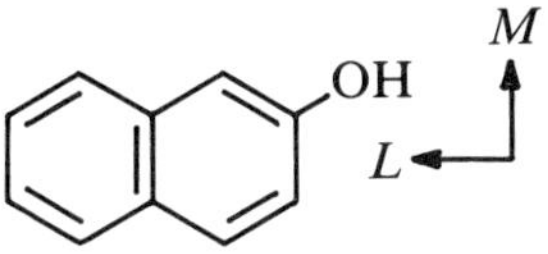

(1) Crystal structure [58]
Monoclinic
$a = 8.185, b = 5.950, c = 36.29$ Å, $\beta = 119.87°$
Space group *Ia*, $Z = 8$ (the unit cell contains two symmetrically independent sets of four molecules).

(2) Molecular geometry [58]
The molecule in the crystal is asymmetric. The detailed shape is not known because of low accuracy in the determination of atomic positions.

(3) Crystal susceptibilities

	⟨χ⟩	χ_1	χ_2	χ_3	ψ
[11]	−97.0	−62.3	−148.3	−80.4	+9.4°
[19]	−97.0	−62.8	−148.1	−80.1	+11.1° (obs)

(4) Orientation of molecular *LMN* axes [19]

	Molecule A			Molecule B		
	a	*b*	c^*	*a*	*b*	c^*
L	−0.400	0.243	0.884	−0.419	−0.162	0.894
M	0.291	−0.892	0.344	0.386	0.861	0.330
N	0.862	0.427	0.272	−0.819	0.495	−0.290

(5) Molecular susceptibilities

	K_L	K_M	K_N
[19]	−63.9	−51.9	−175.2

2.5.25 1-Naphthoic Acid, $C_{10}H_7COOH$

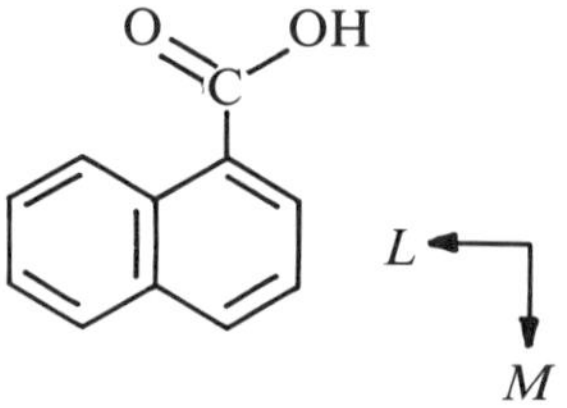

(1) Crystal structure [59]
Monoclinic
$a = 31.12, b = 3.87, c = 6.92$ Å, $\beta = 92.2°$
Space group $P2_1/a$, $Z = 4$

(2) Molecular geometry [59]
The naphthalene ring is planar within ±0.04 Å. One of the two oxygen atoms is situated above and the other below this plane, the deviations being about 0.20 Å. This corresponds to a twist of the carboxylic group by an angle 11° with respect to the plane of the benzene rings.

(3) Crystal susceptibilities

	$\langle\chi\rangle$	χ_1	χ_2	χ_3	θ
[19]	−107.32	−65.25	−85.05	−171.65	−9.95° (obs)

(4) Orientation of molecular *LMN* axes [59]

	a^*	b	c
L	0.7646	0.2472	0.5952
M	0.6441	−0.3217	−0.6939
N	0.0238	0.9152	−0.4022

(5) Molecular susceptibilities

	K_L	K_M	K_N
[19]	−70.5	−58.95	−192.5

2.5.26 1,5-Dinitronaphthalene, $C_{10}H_6(NO_2)_2$

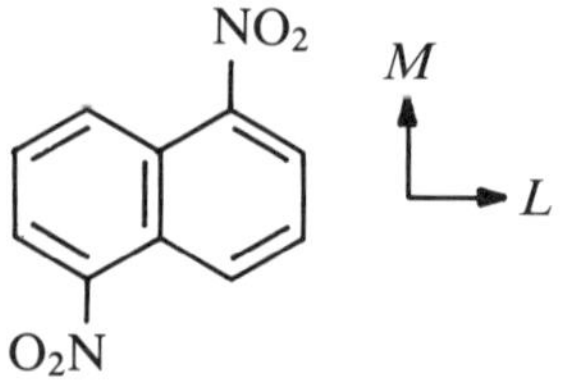

(1) Crystal structure [60]
Monoclinic
$a = 7.76 \pm 0.02, b = 16.32 \pm 0.04, c = 3.70 \pm 0.01$ Å, $\beta = 101.8 \pm 0.2°$
Space group $P2_1/a$, $Z = 2$

(2) Molecular geometry [60]
The molecule has a centre of symmetry; the two nitro groups are each twisted by 48.7° with respect to the plane of the benzene ring.

(3) Crystal susceptibilities

	$\langle\chi\rangle$	χ_1	χ_2	χ_3	ψ
[61]	−107.2	−199.6(1)	−54.6(1)	−67.4(1)	118.2(3)°

(4) Orientation of *LMN* axes of the benzene ring and of *uvw* axes of the nitro group [61]

	L	*M*	*N*	*u*	*v*	*w*
a	0.2132	0.8867	−0.4102	−0.4799	−0.8535	−0.2029
b	−0.8982	0.3431	0.2749	0.7904	−0.3202	−0.5223
c^*	0.3845	0.3098	0.8696	0.3808	−0.4111	0.8282

(5) Molecular susceptibilities

	K_L	K_M	K_N
[61]	−72.52	−49.40	−199.67

(6) Orientation of principal axes of $\boldsymbol{K}$ [61]

	L	*M*	*N*
K_1	−0.9599	−0.1391	0.2433
K_2	−0.0953	0.9784	0.1834
K_3	−0.2636	0.1528	−0.9524

2.5.27 1,8-Dinitronaphthalene, $C_{10}H_6(NO_2)_2$

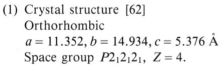

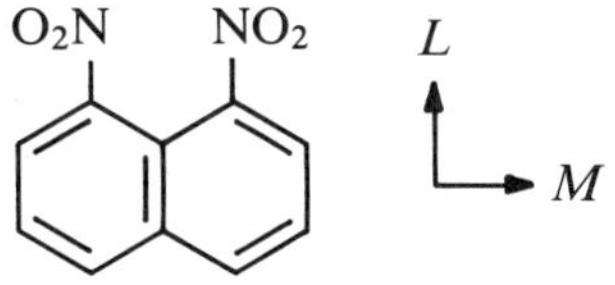

(1) Crystal structure [62]
Orthorhombic
$a = 11.352, b = 14.934, c = 5.376$ Å
Space group $P2_12_12_1$, $Z = 4$.

(2) Molecular geometry [62]
The molecule is asymmetric and non-planar. In particular, the two nitro groups are twisted with respect to the mean plane of the carbon atoms by angles 45.1° and 41.7° in the same sense.

(3) Crystal susceptibilities

	$\langle\chi\rangle$	χ_a	χ_b	χ_c
[13]	−107.2	−168.8	−54.8	−98.0
[24]	−107.2	−170.8	−59.3	−91.4

(4) Orientation of *LMN* axes of the naphthalene nucleus [62]

	a	*b*	*c*
L	0.1047	−0.9742	−0.1997
M	0.6567	−0.0831	0.7495
N	−0.7468	−0.2097	0.6311

(5) Orientation of *uvw* axes of the nitro groups [62]

	u_1	v_1	w_1	u_2	v_2	w_2
a	−0.3618	−0.0097	−0.9320	0.1961	−0.0595	−0.9783
b	0.8885	0.2990	−0.3479	0.9713	0.1487	0.1855
c	0.2822	−0.9540	−0.0996	0.1346	−0.9866	0.0870

(6) Molecular susceptibilities

	K_1	K_2	K_3
[24]	−81.4	−42.8	−197.4

(7) Orientation of principal axes of ***K*** [24]

	L	*M*	*N*
K_1	0.9232	−0.3635	−0.1247
K_2	−0.3825	−0.9003	−0.2077
K_3	0.0341	−0.2384	0.9706

2.5.28 Anthracene, $C_{14}H_{10}$

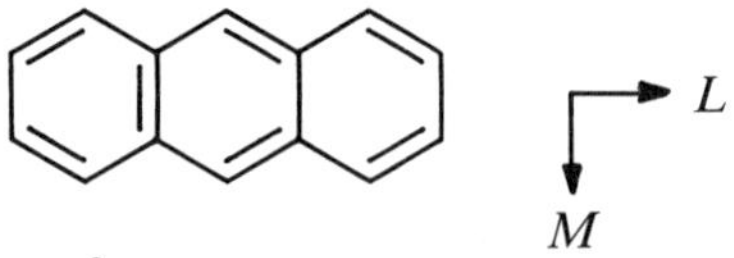

(1) Crystal structure [63]
Monoclinic
$a = 8.562, b = 6.038, c = 11.184$ Å, $\beta = 124.70^\circ$ (290 K)
Space group $P2_1/a$, site group $\bar{1}$, $Z = 2$.

(2) Molecular geometry [63]
The molecule is planar within ±0.004 Å. In the crystal it has *mmm* symmetry.

(3) Crystal susceptibilities

	$\langle\chi\rangle$	χ_1	χ_2	χ_3	ψ
[26]	−130.1	−75.5	−211.8	−102.9	+8.0°
[64]	−134.2	−76.7	−217.0	−108.8	+8.0°
[34]	−130	−72.4 ± 2.0	−212.9 ± 2.0	−104.8 ± 1.0	+9.4 ± 1.1°

(4) Orientation of molecular LMN axes (290 K) [63]

	a	b	c^*
L	−0.4941	−0.1274	0.8600
M	−0.3175	−0.8944	−0.3149
N	0.8094	−0.4287	0.4015

(5) Molecular susceptibilities

	K_L	K_M	K_N
[28]	−75.8	−62.6	−251.8
[64]	−76.9	−76.6	−248.9
[34]	−72.4 ± 2.0	−71.8 ± 1.7	−245.7 ± 2.7

	K_{11}	K_{22}	K_{33}	K_{13}
[24]	−72.42	−73.97	−243.71	+3.08

2.5.29a Anthraquinone (Data 1), $C_{14}H_8O_2$

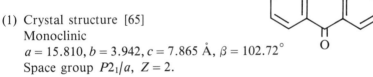

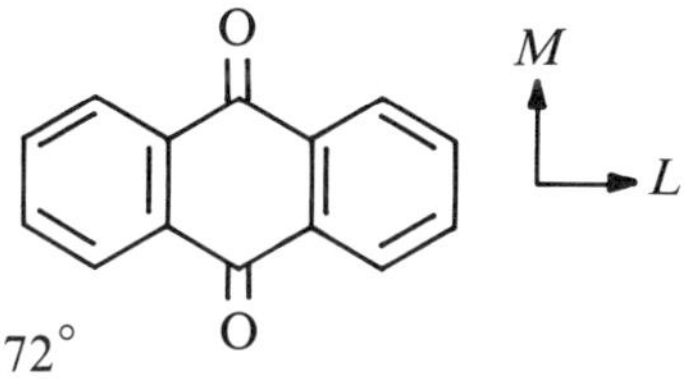

(1) Crystal structure [65]
Monoclinic
$a = 15.810, b = 3.942, c = 7.865$ Å, $\beta = 102.72°$
Space group $P2_1/a$, $Z = 2$.
(2) Molecular geometry [51]
The molecule is planar to high accuracy.
(3) Crystal susceptibilities

	$\langle\chi\rangle$	χ_1	χ_2	χ_3	θ
[19]	−119.6	−64.05	−106.25	−188.50	−37.65°

(4) Orientation of molecular LMN axes [65]

	a	b	c^*
L	0.531	0.451	0.713
M	0.788	0.036	−0.615
N	−0.305	0.889	−0.341

(5) Molecular susceptibilities

	K_L	K_M	K_N
[19]	−76.1	−64.5	−217.9

2.5.29b Anthraquinone (Data 2), $C_{14}H_8O_2$

(1) Crystal structure [66]
Monoclinic
$a = 15.83, b = 3.97, c = 7.89$ Å, $\beta = 102.5°$ (293.8 K)
Space group $P2_1/a$, $Z = 2$.

(2) Molecular geometry [66]
The molecule is planar to high accuracy.

(3) Crystal susceptibilities

	$\langle\chi\rangle$	χ_1	χ_2	χ_3	θ
[19]	−119.6	−63.54	−106.76	−188.50	−43.87° (calc)

(4) Orientation of molecular *LMN* axes calculated from atomic positions at 293.8 K [66, 24]

	a	b	c^*
L	0.5236	0.4870	0.6991
M	−0.7793	−0.0580	0.6240
N	0.3444	−0.8715	0.3492

(5) Molecular susceptibilities

	K_L	K_M	K_N
[24]	−68.9	−63.5	−226.4

2.5.30 Acridine III, $C_{13}H_9N$

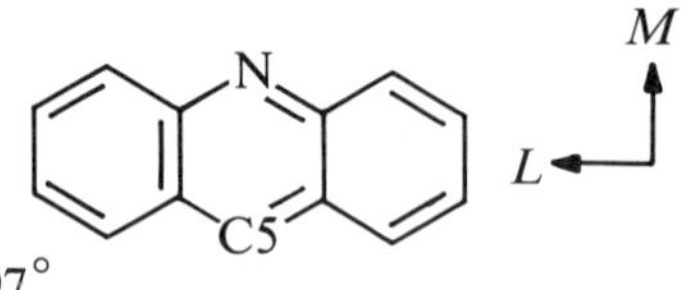

(1) Crystal structure [67]
Monoclinic
$a = 11.375, b = 5.988, c = 13.647$ Å, $\beta = 98.97°$
Space group $P2_1/n$, $Z = 4$.

(2) Molecular geometry [67]
The molecule is bent along N—C5, and the angle between the halves is 2.1°.

(3) Crystal susceptibilities

	$\langle\chi\rangle$	χ_1	χ_2	χ_3	θ
[19]	−123.3	−209.13	−61.33	−99.13	−32.4°

(4) Orientation of molecular *LMN* axes [19]

	a	*b*	c^*
L	0.4725	0.1562	−0.8674
M	0.4369	−0.8962	0.0766
N	0.7652	0.4151	0.4921

(5) Molecular susceptibilities

	K_L	K_M	K_N
[19]	−61.4	−70.5	−238.0

2.5.31 Acridine II, $C_{13}H_9N$

(1) Crystal structure [68]
Monoclinic
$a = 16.292(4)$, $b = 18.831(2)$, $c = 6.072(2)$ Å, $\beta = 95.08(4)^\circ$.
Space group $P2_1/a$, $Z = 8$ (there are two symmetrically independent sets of molecules in the unit cell).

(2) Molecular geometry [68]
Molecule A seems to be non-planar due to a tendency of the central ring to take up a 'chair' configuration but the deviations from planarity are barely significant. Molecule B is bent along N—C19, the halves making an angle of 2° (similar to acridine III).

(3) Crystal susceptibilities

	$\langle\chi\rangle$	χ_1	χ_2	χ_3	ψ
[69]	−123.3	−186.87	−87.77	−95.26	+5.7°

(4) Orientation of molecular *LMN* axes [69]

	Molecule A			Molecule B		
	a	*b*	c^*	*a*	*b*	c^*
L	−0.4421	0.8945	0.0606	−0.4555	0.8651	0.2101
M	0.3247	0.0904	0.9415	−0.3596	−0.3948	0.8455
N	0.8361	0.4379	−0.3304	0.8141	0.3096	0.4909

(5) Molecular susceptibilities

		K_L	K_M	K_N
[69]	Molecule A	−61.6	−65.0	−243.3
[69]	Molecule B	−65.7	−64.4	−239.9

2.5.32 α-Phenazine, $C_{12}H_8N_2$

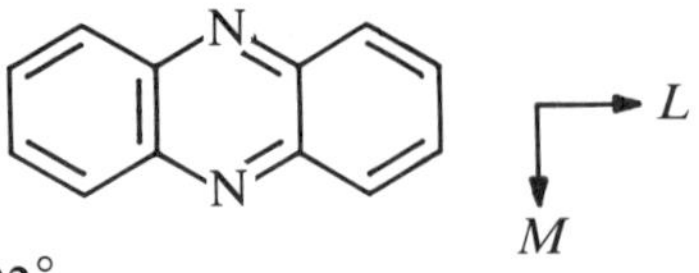

(1) Crystal structure [70]
Monoclinic
$a = 13.22, b = 5.061, c = 7.088$ Å, $\beta = 109.22°$
Space group $P2_1/a$, $Z = 2$.
Molecules are grouped in stacks along [010] with their planes parallel to each other at a mean distance of 3.49 Å. The crystal structure is similar to that of anthracene.

(2) Molecular geometry [70]
The molecule is planar within experimental error. Its symmetry in the free state is *mmm*, and in the crystal $\bar{1}$.

(3) Crystal susceptibilities

	$\langle\chi\rangle$	χ_1	χ_2	χ_3	ψ
[71]	−117	−60.8 ± 2	−150.0 ± 2	−140.2 ± 2	−14.8°

(4) Orientation of molecular *LMN* axes [24]

	a	*b*	*c**
L	0.4029	0.6979	0.5921
M	−0.6852	−0.1989	0.7006
N	0.6064	−0.6886	0.3976

(5) Molecular susceptibilities

	K_L	K_M	K_N
[71]	−46.2	−61.8	−243.0
[24]	−47.6	−61.8	−241.6

2.5.33 Glycine, $CH_2(NH_2)COOH$

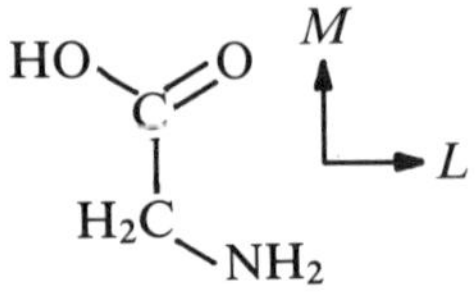

(1) Crystal structure [72]
Monoclinic
$a = 5.102, b = 11.97, c = 5.4575$ Å, $\beta = 111.7°$
Space group $P2_1/n$, $Z = 4$.

(2) Molecular geometry [72]
The carbon and oxygen atoms are situated in one plane, approximately.

(3) Crystal susceptibilities

	$\langle\chi\rangle$	χ_1	χ_2	χ_3	ψ
[34]	−40.3	−37.67(8)	−39.37(8)	−43.87(13)	+48.0 ± 1.1° (obs)

(4) Orientation of molecular *LMN* axes (carbon and oxygen atoms) [34]

	a^*	b	c
L	0.8739	−0.2903	0.3899
M	0.4127	0.0195	−0.9105
N	0.2616	0.9550	0.1390

(5) Molecular susceptibilities

	K_L	K_M	K_N
[34]	−36.92(10)	−39.40(8)	−44.68(15)

2.5.34a Barbituric Acid (Data 1), $C_4H_4N_2O_3 \cdot 2H_2O$

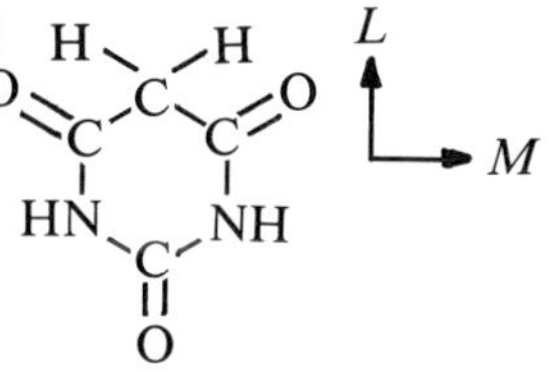

(1) Crystal structure [73]
Orthorhombic
$a = 12.74, b = 6.24, c = 8.89$ Å
Space group *Pnma*, $Z = 4$.
Acid and water molecules are situated on (010) mirror planes forming a hydrogen-bonded lattice. The normals to the planes of the two kinds of molecules are both parallel to the crystallographic *b* axis.

(2) Molecular geometry [73]
The molecule of barbituric acid has the form of a triketone and in the crystal has the symmetry *mm*.

(3) Crystal susceptibilities

	$\langle\chi\rangle$	χ_a	χ_b	χ_c
[19]	−78.6	−73.1	−90.6	−72.2

(4) Orientation of molecular *LMN* axes [73]

	a	b	c
L	0.7650	0	0.6439
M	−0.6440	0	0.7651
N	0	1	0

(5) Molecular susceptibilities

	K_L	K_M	K_N
[19]	−75.3	−70.0	−90.6

2.5.34b Barbituric Acid (Data 2)

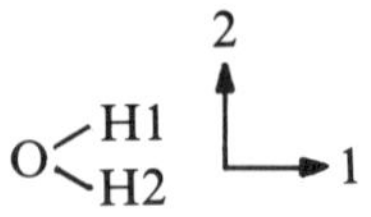

(3) Crystal susceptibilities

	⟨χ⟩	χ_a	χ_b	χ_c
[19]	−78.6	−73.1	−90.6	−72.2

(4) Orientation of molecular *LMN* axes of acid molecule [24]

	a	*b*	*c*
⟨*L*⟩	0.7581	0	0.6522
⟨*M*⟩	0.6522	0	−0.7581
N	0	1	0

(5) Orientation of 1, 2, 3 axes of water molecules [24]

	a	*b*	*c*	*a*	*b*	*c*
1	0.1642	0	−0.9864	−0.9540	0	0.2999
2	−0.9864	0	−0.1642	0.2999	0	0.9540
3	0	1	0	0	1	0

(6) Susceptibilities of water molecule

	K_1	K_2	K_3
[74]	−13.5 ± 2.0	−12.1 ± 1.6	−13.7 ± 1.8
[75]	−13.7 ± 0.3	−12.1 ± 0.05	−12.7 ± 0.1

(7) Molecular susceptibilities of the acid molecule

	K_L	K_M	K_N
[24]	−50.51	−43.15	−65.20

2.5.35 *N*-Chlorosuccinimide (NCS), $C_4H_4O_2NCl$

2.5.36 *N*-Bromosuccinimide (NBS), $C_4H_4O_2NBr$

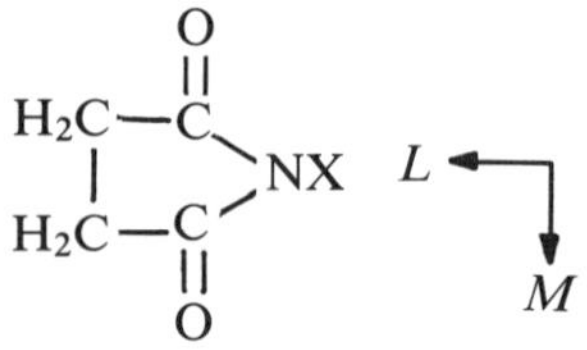

(1) Crystal structure [76]
Orthorhombic; structures are isomorphic

	a	*b*	*c*	Space group	*Z*
NCS	6.41	7.11	11.9 Å	$P2_12_12_1$	4
NBS	6.48	7.25	11.86 Å	$P2_12_12_1$	4

(2) Molecular geometry [76]
The molecules are planar within experimental error.
(3) Crystal susceptibilities

		$\langle\chi\rangle$	χ_a	χ_b	χ_c
NCS	[19]	−64.38	−59.1	−72.6	−62.1
NBS	[19]	−74.96	−69.3	−82.3	−72.3

(4) Orientation of *LMN* axes (the same for NCS and NBS) [76]

	a	*b*	*c*
L	0.3569	0.2612	−0.8967
M	0.8062	0.3987	0.4370
N	−0.4732	0.8783	0.0675

(5) Molecular susceptibilities

		K_L	K_M	K_N
NCS	[19]	−64.50	−51.76	−76.96
NBS	[19]	−76.03	−61.57	−87.31

2.5.37 Parabanic Acid, $CO(NHCO)_2$

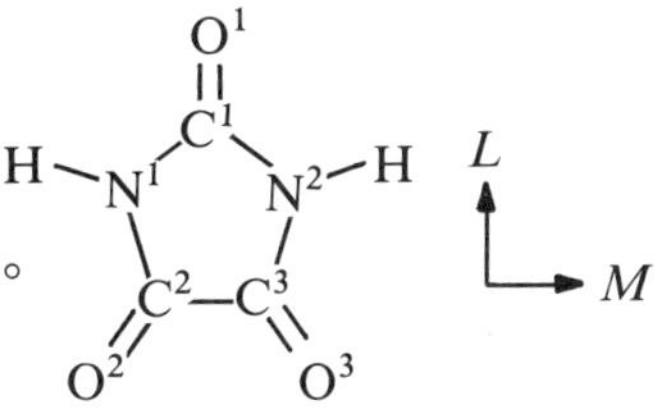

(1) Crystal structure [77]
Monoclinic
$a = 10.685, b = 8.194, c = 5.054$ Å, $\beta = 92.73°$
Space group $P2_1/n$, $Z = 4$.
(2) Molecular geometry [77]
The best plane can be set through the five ring atoms. The oxygen atom O3 is not significantly displaced from this plane but atoms O1 and O2 show significant deviations.
(3) Crystal susceptibilities

	$\langle\chi\rangle$	χ_1	χ_2	χ_3	ψ
[19]	−35.34	−27.5	−35.8	−42.7	−76.6° (obs)

(4) Orientation of molecular *LMN* axes [19]

	a	*b*	c^*
$L \parallel$ C1O1	0.0547	0.5758	−0.8158
$M \parallel$ O2O3	−0.9904	0.1191	0.0176
N	0.1076	0.8094	0.5768

(5) Molecular susceptibilities

	K_L	K_M	K_N
[19]	−28.6	−27.5	−49.9

2.5.38 Hydrogen Ammonium-*d*-tartrate (AHT), $C_4H_4O_6(NH_4)H$

2.5.39 Hydrogen Potassium-*d*-tartrate (KHT), $C_4H_4O_6KH$

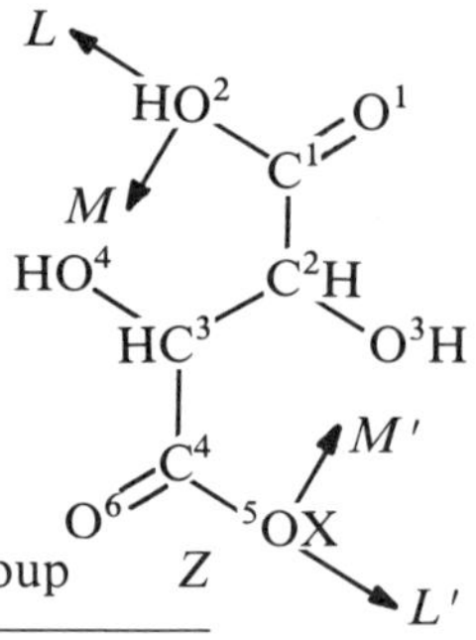

(1) Crystal structure [78]
Orthorhombic; the structures are isomorphous.

	a	*b*	*c*	Space group	*Z*
AHT	7.648	11.066	7.843 Å	$P2_12_12_1$	4
KHT	7.64	10.62	7.75 Å	$P2_12_12_1$	4

(2) Molecular geometry [78]
As in the crystal structures of all tartrates so far examined, the carbon chain and the oxygen atoms of each half (—CH(OH)COOH) of the tartaric molecule are nearly planar.

(3) Crystal susceptibilities

		$\langle\chi\rangle$	χ_a	χ_b	χ_c
AHT	[19]	−81.85	−77.23	−84.91	−83.42
KHT	[19]	−83.07	−78.46	−86.15	−84.61

(4) Orientation of molecular *LMN* axes (the same for AHT and KHT) [19]. The system of axes is referred to the orientation of carboxylic groups: $L \parallel$ C1–O2, $L' \parallel$ C4–O5, $M \perp$ C1–O2 and in plane of C1–O1–O2, $M' \perp$ C4–O5 and in plane of C4–O5–O6, $N \perp L, M$, $N' \perp L', M'$.

	a	*b*	*c*		*a*	*b*	*c*
L	0.3773	0.8325	0.4056	*L′*	0.7324	−0.1655	−0.6605
M	0.8684	−0.4702	0.1574	*M′*	0.6786	0.0988	0.7278
N	0.3218	0.2929	−0.9005	*N′*	0.0551	0.9808	−0.1845

(5) Molecular susceptibilities for one half of the molecule, i.e. containing the group —CH(OH)COO· and a 'mean' substituent, (X, H)/2.

		K_L	K_M	K_N
AHT	[19]	−37.41	−38.57	−46.80
KHT	[19]	−38.31	−39.04	−47.26

2.5.40 Chloroacetamide, $CH_2ClCO(NH_2)$

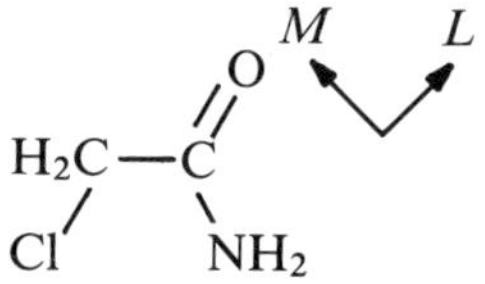

(1) Crystal structure [79]
Chloroacetamide is polymorphic. The magnetic properties have been investigated of the particular polymorph which crystallizes from ethanol.
Monoclinic
$a = 10.26, b = 5.14, c = 7.41$ Å, $\beta = 98.82°$
Space group $P2_1/c$, $Z = 4$.

(2) Molecular geometry [79]
In this polymorph the molecules are nearly planar.

(3) Crystal susceptibilities

	$\langle\chi\rangle$	χ_1	χ_2	χ_3	ψ
[19]	−51.27	−49.01	−53.74	−51.06	−55.5° (obs)

(4) Orientation of the molecular *LMN* axes [19]

	a	*b*	*c*
L (∥ C=O)	0.3516	−0.9190	−0.1780
M (⊥ C=O)	0.8890	0.3873	−0.2439
N	0.2788	−0.0355	0.9597

(5) Molecular susceptibilities

	K_L	K_M	K_N
[19]	−51.70	−48.74	−53.37

2.6 REFERENCES

1. André Michel, *Phénomènes Magnétiques*, Masson, Paris, 1966.
2. S. V. Vonsovskii, *Magnetism*, Wiley, New York, 1974.
3. J. F. Nye, *Physical Properties of Crystals*, Clarendon, Oxford, 1957.
4. P. W. Selwood, *Magnetochemistry*, Interscience, New York, 1963.
5. P. W. Selwood, in *Physical Methods of Organic Chemistry*, Vol. 1, Part III (ed. A. Weissberger), Wiley-Interscience, New York, 1954.
6. J. H. Van Vleck, *The Theory of Electric and Magnetic Susceptibilities*, University Press, Oxford, 1932.
7. J. G. Dorfmann, *Diamagnetismus und chemische Bindung*, Deutsch, Frankfurt/Main, 1964.
8. L. F. Bates, *Modern Magnetism*, 4th edn, University Press, Cambridge, 1961.
9. B. Staliński, *Magnetochemia*, Panstwowe Wydawnictwo Naukowe, Warsaw, 1966.
10. J. L. Friar and S. Fallieros, *Am. J. Phys.*, **49**, 847 (1981).
11. L. G. Gouy, *C.R. Acad. Sci., Paris*, **109**, 935 (1889).
12. B. L. Morris, *Rev. Sci. Inst.*, **39**, 1937 (1968).
13. K. S. Krishnan, B. C. Guha and S. Banerjee, *Phil. Trans.*, **A231**, 235 (1933).

14. K. S. Krishnan and S. Banerjee, *Phil. Trans. Roy. Soc.*, **A234**, 265 (1935).
15. A. Mierzejewski, unpublished results.
16. *International Critical Tables* **6**, 362, 364 (1929).
17. J. A. Pople, *J. Chem. Phys.*, **24**, 1111 (1956).
18. M. A. Lasheen, *Phil. Trans. Roy. Soc. Lond.*, **A256**, 357 (1964).
19. J. Rohleder, *Fizyka chemiczna kryształów molekularnych*, Panstwowe Wydawnictwo Naukowe, Warsaw, 1989.
20. E. G. Cox, D. W. J. Cruickshank and J. A. S. Smith, *Proc. Roy. Soc. (Lond.)*, **A247**, 1 (1958).
21. S. M. Kochubei, *Opt. Spektr.*, **17**, 213 (1964).
22. J. Hoarau, N. Lumbroso and A. Pacault, *C.R. Acad. Sci.*, **242**, 1702 (1956).
23. A. Pacault, B. Lemanceau and J. Joussot-Dubien, *C.R. Acad. Sci.*, **242**, 1305 (1956).
24. J. W. Rohleder, own computations (1982).
25. J. Trotter, *Acta Cryst.*, **13**, 86 (1960).
26. K. Lonsdale and K. S. Krishnan, *Proc. Roy. Soc.*, **A156**, 597 (1936).
27. S. S. C. Chu, G. A. Jeffrey and T. Sakurai, *Acta Cryst.*, **15**, 661 (1962).
28. S. Banerjee, *Z Kristallogr.*, **A100**, 316 (1938).
29. T. Sakurai, *Acta Cryst.*, **15**, 443 (1962).
30. U. Croatto, S. Bezzi and E. Bua, *Acta Cryst.*, **5**, 825 (1952).
31. A. Klug, *Nature*, **160**, 57 (1947).
32. S. Bezzi and U. Croatto, *Gazz. Chim. Ital.*, **72**, 318 (1942).
33. T. H. Goodwin, M. Przybylska and J. M. Robertson, *Acta Cryst.*, **3**, 279 (1950).
34. M. A. Lasheen, *Acta Cryst.*, **A24**, 289 (1968).
35. J. Trotter, *Acta Cryst.*, **14**, 244 (1961).
36. P. Coppens, *Structure and Lightsensitivity of the Crystals of Some Aromatic Nitro Compounds*, Thesis, Amsterdam, 1960.
37. J. Jarmakowicz and J. W. Rohleder, *Acta Phys. Polon.*, **35**, 897 (1959).
38. G. M. Brown and O. A. W. Strydom, *Acta Cryst.*, **B30**, 801 (1974).
39. G. Fulińska-Wójcik and J. W. Rohleder, *Acta Phys. Polon.*, **A45**, 3 (1974).
40. A. Tulinsky and J. G. White, *Acta Cryst.*, **11**, 7 (1958).
41. T. Sakurai, *Acta Cryst.*, **15**, 1164 (1962).
42. J. Meinnel, Y. Balcou and P. Gregoire, *Proc Colloq. Ampère*, **12**, 429 (1963).
43. J. W. Rohleder and B. Jakubowski, *Acta Phys. Polon.*, **31**, 1047 (1967).
44. G. A. Sim, J. M. Robertson and T. H. Goodwin, *Acta Cryst.*, **8**, 157 (1955).
45. J. Jarmakowicz and J. W. Rohleder, *Acta Phys. Polon.*, **28**, 513 (1965).
46. K. Venkateswarlu and S. Sriraman, *Trans. Faraday Soc.*, **53**, 433 (1957).
47. F. M. French, *Trans. Faraday Soc.*, **50**, 1320 (1954).
48. C. J. Brown and D. E. C. Corbridge, *Acta Cryst.*, **7**, 711 (1954).
49. K. N. Trueblood, E. Goldish and J. Donohue, *Acta Cryst.*, **14**, 1009 (1961).
50. J. W. Rohleder, *Zesz. Nauk. Politechn. Wrocław, Chemia*, **24**, 19 (1969).
51. G. H. Goldschmidt and F. J. Llewellyn, *Acta Cryst.*, **3**, 294 (1950).
52. Y. Okaya and R. Pepinsky, *Acta Cryst.*, **10**, 324 (1957).
53. D. W. J. Cruickshank, *Acta Cryst.*, **10**, 504 (1957).
54. J. Trotter, *Acta Cryst.*, **14**, 1135 (1961).
55. A. Hargreaves and S. Hasan Rizvi, *Acta Cryst.*, **15**, 365 (1962).
56. G. P. Charbonneau and Y. Delugeard, *Acta Cryst.*, **B33**, 1586 (1977).
57. H. W. W. Ehrlich, *Acta Cryst.*, **10**, 699 (1957).
58. A. Hargreaves and H. C. Watson, *Acta Cryst.*, **11**, 556 (1958).
59. J. Trotter, *Acta Cryst.*, **13**, 732 (1960).
60. J. Trotter, *Acta Cryst.*, **13**, 95 (1960).
61. J. W. Rohleder and A. Mierzejewski, *Materials Sci.*, **4**, 97 (1978).
62. Z. A. Akopian, A. I. Kitaigorodskii and Yu. T. Strutchkov, *J. Strukt. Chem. SSSR*, **6**, 729 (1965).

63. R. Mason, *Acta Cryst.*, **17**, 547 (1964).
64. N. Lumbroso-Bader, *Ann. Chim.*, **13**, 687 (1956).
65. B. V. R. Murty, *Z. Kristallogr.*, **113**, 445 (1960).
66. K. Lonsdale, H. J. Milledge and K. El Sayed, *Acta Cryst.*, **20**, 1 (1966).
67. D. C. Phillips, *Acta Cryst.*, **9**, 237 (1956).
68. D. C. Phillips, F. R. Ahmed and W. H. Barnes, *Acta Cryst.*, **13**, 365 (1960).
69. R. Burzyński, Thesis, Wrocław, 1981.
70. F. H. Herbstein and G. M. J. Schmidt, *Acta Cryst.*, **8**, 399 (1955).
71. F. H. Herbstein and G. M. J. Schmidt, *Acta Cryst.*, **8**, 406 (1955).
72. R. E. Marsh, *Acta Cryst.*, **11**, 654 (1958).
73. G. A. Jeffrey, S. Ghose and J. D. Warwicker, *Acta Cryst.*, **14**, 881 (1961).
74. H. Taft and B. P. Dailey, *J. Chem. Phys.*, **51**, 1002 (1969).
75. Yen-Chi Pan and H. F. Hameka, *J. Chem. Phys.*, **53**, 1265 (1970).
76. R. N. Brown, *Acta Cryst.*, **14**, 711 (1961).
77. D. R. Davies and J. J. Blum, *Acta Cryst.*, **8**, 129 (1955).
78. A. J. Van Bommel and J. M. Bijvoet, *Acta Cryst.*, **11**, 61 (1958).
79. J. Dejace, *Acta Cryst.*, **8**, 851 (1955).

3 Optics

3.1 BASIC CONCEPTS

Broad treatments of macroscopic optics are given in a variety of texts [1–3] and more advanced monographs [4–6]. For present purposes we shall mainly be concerned with plane wave solutions of Maxwell's equations of electromagnetism propagating in an anisotropic dielectric medium. The principal characteristic of the wave to be investigated is the refractive index and how it varies with the direction in the crystal.

Maxwell's equations are conveniently written as follows when dealing with dielectric materials:

$$\text{div } \boldsymbol{D} = \rho_f \tag{3.1.1}$$

$$\text{curl } \boldsymbol{E} = -\frac{\partial \boldsymbol{B}}{\partial t} \tag{3.1.2}$$

$$\text{div } \boldsymbol{B} = 0 \tag{3.1.3}$$

$$\text{curl } \boldsymbol{H} = j_f + \frac{\partial \boldsymbol{D}}{\partial t}. \tag{3.1.4}$$

Here ρ_f and j_f are the free or mobile charge and current densities, while as usual $\boldsymbol{D}$ denotes the electric displacement (which is continuous across the boundary between different media), $\boldsymbol{E}$ the electric field, $\boldsymbol{B}$ the magnetic induction, and $\boldsymbol{H}$ the magnetic field. We shall treat only insulating media, so that ρ_f and j_f are zero. We shall also treat only weak magnetic media (as in Section 2), so that the relative permeability $\mu_r \approx 1$ and $\boldsymbol{B} \approx \mu_0 \boldsymbol{H}$. Then Maxwell's equations reduce to

$$\text{div } \boldsymbol{D} = 0 \tag{3.1.5}$$

$$\text{curl } \boldsymbol{E} = -\mu_0 \frac{\partial \boldsymbol{H}}{\partial t} \tag{3.1.6}$$

$$\text{div } \boldsymbol{H} = 0 \tag{3.1.7}$$

$$\text{curl } \boldsymbol{H} = \frac{\partial \boldsymbol{D}}{\partial t}, \tag{3.1.8}$$

where we have chosen to eliminate $\boldsymbol{B}$ in favour of $\boldsymbol{H}$. It is known that this set of equations has solutions in the form of plane waves, and we now explore the nature of these solutions.

A particular plane-wave solution can be written as

$$\boldsymbol{E} = \boldsymbol{E}_0 \exp[i\omega(t - \boldsymbol{r}\cdot\boldsymbol{l}/v)]. \tag{3.1.9}$$

Here ω is the angular frequency of the vibrations of $\boldsymbol{E}$, $\boldsymbol{r}$ is the position at time t, $\boldsymbol{l}$ is the unit vector normal to a plane of constant phase and v is the phase velocity. These vectors are illustrated in Figure 3.1, where π represents a plane of constant phase. If we draw a vector $\boldsymbol{r}$ from an arbitrary point 0 to the plane π, we see that the equation of π can be written as

$$\boldsymbol{r}\cdot\boldsymbol{l} = \text{constant} = \text{ON} \tag{3.1.10}$$

where N is the point on π through which the perpendicular from O passes. Thus ON is the distance from O to π and v is the velocity with which π moves along ON.

Substituting (3.1.9) in (3.1.6) and integrating over time, we obtain

$$\mu_0 \boldsymbol{H} = \frac{1}{v}\boldsymbol{l}\times\boldsymbol{E} \tag{3.1.11}$$

$$\boldsymbol{H} = \boldsymbol{H}_0 \exp[i\omega(t - \boldsymbol{r}\cdot\boldsymbol{l}/v)] \tag{3.1.12}$$

where the cross in (3.1.11) denotes a vector product. These equations show that in a dielectric medium, $\boldsymbol{H}$ also takes the form of a plane wave, in phase with $\boldsymbol{E}$ but vibrating perpendicular to $\boldsymbol{E}$ within a given plane of constant phase so that $\boldsymbol{H}$, $\boldsymbol{l}$ and $\boldsymbol{E}$ form a right-handed triple of vectors. Details of this calculation can be found elsewhere [4, 6].

Similarly, from (3.1.8) we obtain

$$\boldsymbol{D} = -\frac{1}{v}\boldsymbol{l}\times\boldsymbol{H} \tag{3.1.13}$$

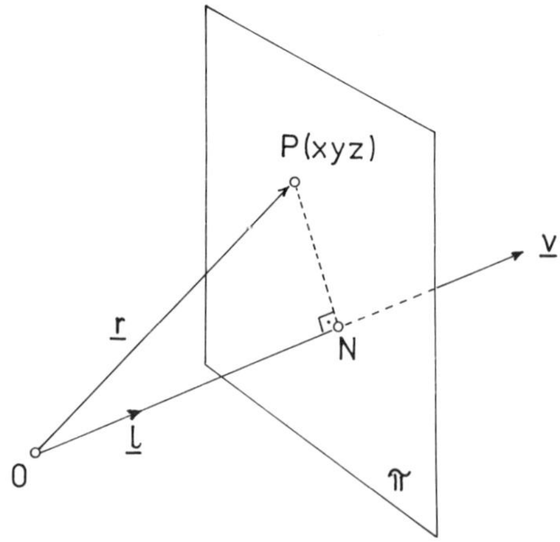

Figure 3.1. A plane of constant phase, π

so that $-\boldsymbol{D}$, $\boldsymbol{l}$ and $\boldsymbol{H}$ also form a right-handed triple of vectors. The general disposition in space of all the vectors describing the state of an electromagnetic wave in a non-magnetic medium is presented in Figure 3.2 [4]. With our assumption $\mu_r = 1$, $\boldsymbol{B}$ is parallel to $\boldsymbol{H}$, but in general the vectors $\boldsymbol{D}$ and $\boldsymbol{E}$ are not parallel; the magnitude and physical significance of the angle ξ between $\boldsymbol{D}$ and $\boldsymbol{E}$ will be discussed later. The vector $\boldsymbol{S}$ in Figure 3.2 is the *Poynting vector*, describing the magnitude and direction of the energy flux transferred by the wave motion. Energy flows with the velocity $\boldsymbol{u}$ which in general differs from the phase velocity v, as shown in the figure.

Finally and most importantly it remains to relate $\boldsymbol{D}$ and $\boldsymbol{E}$. By substituting (3.1.11) into (3.1.13) we find

$$\boldsymbol{D} = -\frac{1}{\mu_0 v^2}\,\boldsymbol{l}\times(\boldsymbol{l}\times\boldsymbol{E}) \tag{3.1.14}$$

which can be rewritten as

$$\boldsymbol{D} = -\frac{1}{\mu_0 v^2}\,[\boldsymbol{l}(\boldsymbol{l}\cdot\boldsymbol{E}) - \boldsymbol{E}] \tag{3.1.15}$$

using the vector identity

$$\boldsymbol{A}\times(\boldsymbol{B}\times\boldsymbol{C}) = \boldsymbol{B}(\boldsymbol{A}\cdot\boldsymbol{C}) - \boldsymbol{C}(\boldsymbol{A}\cdot\boldsymbol{B}). \tag{3.1.16}$$

So far only Maxwell's equations have been used together with the form of a plane-wave solution. To make further progress we need the constitutive relation between $\boldsymbol{D}$ and $\boldsymbol{E}$ characteristic of the medium in question. For a general anisotropic medium this takes the form

$$\boldsymbol{D} = \varepsilon_0 \boldsymbol{\epsilon} \boldsymbol{E}, \tag{3.1.17}$$

where ε_0 is the permittivity of free space and $\boldsymbol{\epsilon}$ is the relative permittivity tensor of the medium at the optical frequency ω. In the principal axis system

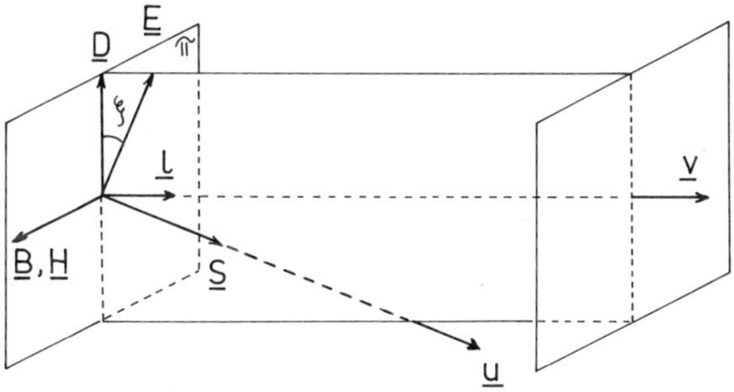

Figure 3.2. Spatial relations between vectors describing the state of an electromagnetic wave

of ϵ, (3.1.17) takes the straightforward form

$$D_i = \varepsilon_0 \varepsilon_i E_i \qquad (i = 1, 2, 3), \tag{3.1.18}$$

where all ε_i must be positive. Use of the principal axis system facilitates subsequent analysis and interpretation.

Substituting (3.1.18) in (3.1.15), we obtain

$$\left(\varepsilon_0 \varepsilon_i - \frac{1}{\mu_0 v^2}\right) E_i + \frac{1}{\mu_0 v^2} l_i (\boldsymbol{l} \cdot \boldsymbol{E}) = 0. \tag{3.1.19}$$

To investigate the solutions of this equation, let us choose the simple case $\boldsymbol{l} = (1\ \ 0\ \ 0)$ where the normal to the plane of constant phase of the wave which enters the crystal lies parallel to the principal axis X_1 of ϵ in the crystal. Putting $i = 1, 2, 3$ in turn in (3.1.19) we find the following equations for the components of $\boldsymbol{E}$:

$$\left(\varepsilon_0 \varepsilon_1 - \frac{1}{\mu_0 v^2}\right) E_1 + \frac{1}{\mu_0 v^2} E_1 = 0 \tag{3.1.20}$$

$$\left(\varepsilon_0 \varepsilon_2 - \frac{1}{\mu_0 v^2}\right) E_2 = 0 \tag{3.1.21}$$

$$\left(\varepsilon_0 \varepsilon_3 - \frac{1}{\mu_0 v^2}\right) E_3 = 0. \tag{3.1.22}$$

The first of these equations leads to the conclusion that $E_1 = 0$: we cannot have a component of $\boldsymbol{E}$ along the direction of the phase velocity in a transverse wave. The other two equations give

$$v_k = (\varepsilon_0 \mu_0 \varepsilon_k)^{-1/2} \qquad (k = 2, 3). \tag{3.1.23}$$

Therefore for a wave incident along $\boldsymbol{l} = (1\ \ 0\ \ 0)$ we can have two waves travelling in the crystal, one with the vibration direction along the principal axis X_2 and the other along X_3, with velocities given by (3.1.23). Analogous conclusions are obtained for $\boldsymbol{l} = (0\ \ 1\ \ 0)$ or $\boldsymbol{l} = (0\ \ 0\ \ 1)$. Since it is known that

$$(\varepsilon_0 \mu_0)^{-1/2} = c \tag{3.1.24}$$

where c is the speed of light *in vacuo* then equations (3.1.23) and their analogues for other principal directions of incidence can be written as

$$v_i = c/\varepsilon_i^{1/2} = c/n_i \qquad (i = 1, 2, 3). \tag{3.1.25}$$

Here n_i is a principal index of refraction, which relates the phase velocity to the velocity of light; we see that

$$\varepsilon_i = n_i^2. \tag{3.1.26}$$

The refractive indices are always positive, and except in frequency regions associated with absorption, where anomalous dispersion may occur, they are greater than unity.

3.2 INDICATRIX

The quadric of the dielectric permittivity tensor is given by an equation analogous to (1.3.2)

$$r^{\mathrm{T}}\boldsymbol{\epsilon}r = 1. \tag{3.2.1}$$

In the principal axes system $\boldsymbol{\epsilon}$ is diagonal. Denoting the components of r by $x_1x_2x_3$ we have

$$(x_1x_2x_3)\begin{pmatrix}\varepsilon_1 & 0 & 0\\ 0 & \varepsilon_2 & 0\\ 0 & 0 & \varepsilon_3\end{pmatrix}\begin{pmatrix}x_1\\ x_2\\ x_3\end{pmatrix} = x_1^2\varepsilon_1 + x_2^2\varepsilon_2 + x_3^2\varepsilon_3 = 1. \tag{3.2.2}$$

In a spectral region remote from any anomalous dispersion all ε_i are greater than unity and then equation (3.2.2) represents an ellipsoid shown in Figure 3.3 with the semi-axes A_i, $i = 1, 2, 3$, given by (1.3.7) and (3.1.26) so that

$$A_i = \frac{1}{\varepsilon_i^{1/2}} = \frac{1}{n_i}. \tag{3.2.3}$$

This ellipsoid which is described by the equation

$$\sum \frac{x_i^2}{n_i^2} = 1 \tag{3.2.4}$$

plays an important role in the optics of anisotropic media and is called the *indicatrix*. We see that the principal axes of the indicatrix are identical with those of the permittivity tensor and its semi-axes are equal to the principal refractive indices of the material.

The length of the vector r in (3.2.1) can easily be calculated. If we choose a unit vector $l(l_1l_2l_3)$ in the direction or r, we have $x_i = |r|\, l_i$ and

$$\sum \frac{x_i^2}{n_i^2} = r^2 \qquad \sum \frac{l_i^2}{n_i^2} = 1.$$

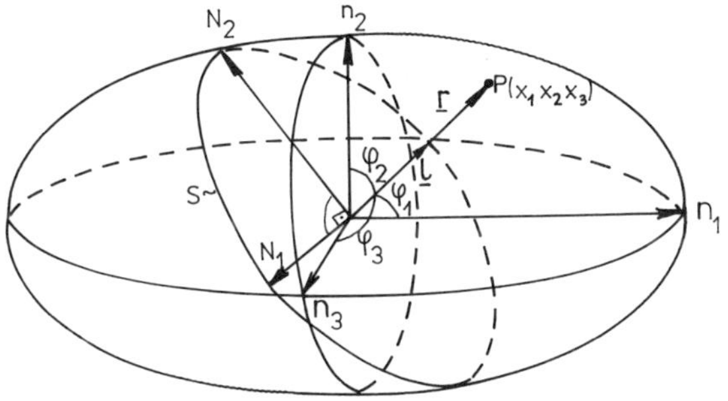

Figure 3.3. Triaxial indicatrix

Therefore,

$$\sum \frac{l_i^2}{n_i^2} = \frac{1}{r^2} \equiv \frac{1}{N_1^2}. \tag{3.2.5}$$

The length of $\boldsymbol{r}$ determines the refractive index in the direction $\boldsymbol{l}$: $N_l \equiv |\boldsymbol{r}|$. (We use capital N for a refractive index in an arbitrary direction to distinguish it from the principal refractive indices.) Note that in spite of the fact that the indicatrix has the property of a surface of magnitude expressed in (3.2.5), the refractive index itself is not a tensor quantity: we may write an equation analogous to (1.3.7) for dielectric permittivity but we cannot do so for the refractive index.

Each central section S of the indicatrix, i.e. each section containing the origin of coordinates in its plane, is in general an ellipse. The semi-axes of the ellipse N_1 and N_2 (Figure 3.3) are the refractive indices which determine the velocities of the two waves which are allowed to travel through the crystal for the given direction of incidence $\boldsymbol{l}$ perpendicular to S. These two waves oscillate with the electric displacement $\boldsymbol{D}$ parallel to N_1 or N_2. Any beam of radiation incident parallel to $\boldsymbol{l}$ which is polarized in a direction such that $\boldsymbol{D}$ is not parallel to N_1 or N_2 cannot travel in the crystal as a single beam: at the crystal surface it will divide into two beams polarized parallel to N_1 and N_2, travelling independently of one another with different velocities. This is the phenomenon of double refraction.

The properties of sections of the indicatrix can also be shown analytically from (3.1.19). Let us choose first a section with its normal $\boldsymbol{l}$ perpendicular to the X_3 principal axis, so that $\boldsymbol{l} = (\cos\phi, \sin\phi, 0)$ as shown in Figure 3.4. As ϕ varies, $\boldsymbol{l}$ scans through all directions in the X_1X_2 plane. From equation

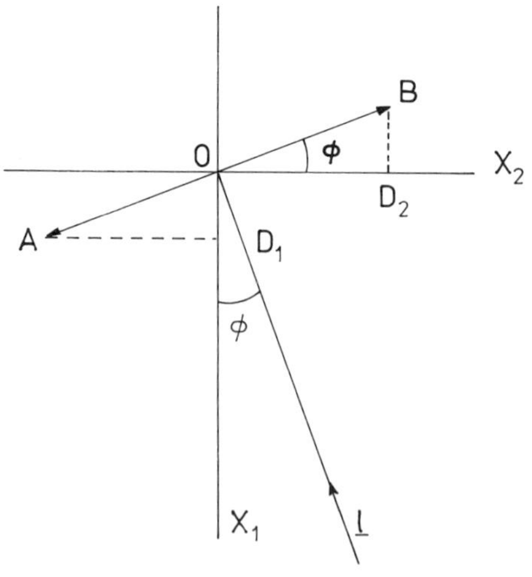

Figure 3.4. Components of the vector $\boldsymbol{D}$ of a wave travelling in the direction of the wave-normal, **l**

(3.1.19) we have for $i = 1, 2$

$$\left(\varepsilon_0\varepsilon_i - \frac{1}{\mu_0 v^2}\right)E_i + \frac{l_i}{\mu_0 v^2}(E_1 \cos\phi + E_2 \sin\phi) = 0 \tag{3.2.6}$$

and for $i = 3$

$$\left(\varepsilon_0\varepsilon_3 - \frac{1}{\mu_0 v^2}\right)E_3 = 0. \tag{3.2.7}$$

The latter equation yields at once the previous result, $\varepsilon_3 = c^2/v_3^2 = n_3^2$. In equation (3.2.6) we set

$$\frac{1}{\varepsilon_0\mu_0 v^2} = \frac{c^2}{v^2} \equiv N^2 \tag{3.2.8}$$

where N is the refractive index. Then after rearrangement we obtain the two homogeneous equations

$$(\varepsilon_1 - N^2 \sin^2\phi)E_1 + N^2 \sin\phi \cos\phi \; E_2 = 0 \tag{3.2.9}$$

$$N^2 \sin\phi \cos\phi \; E_1 + (\varepsilon_2 - N^2 \cos^2\phi)E_2 = 0. \tag{3.2.10}$$

The existence of simultaneous solutions of these equations for non-zero E_1 and E_2 requires that the characteristic determinant should vanish, leading to the condition

$$\frac{1}{N^2} = \frac{\cos^2\phi}{\varepsilon_2} + \frac{\sin^2\phi}{\varepsilon_1} \tag{3.2.11}$$

$$= \frac{\cos^2\phi}{n_2^2} + \frac{\sin^2\phi}{n_1^2}. \tag{3.2.12}$$

The last form is seen to be a special case of (3.2.5) which gives the refractive index along the line AB in Figure 3.4 corresponding to the intersection of the plane of constant phase perpendicular to $\boldsymbol{l}$ with the X_1X_2 plane. Substituting (3.2.11) into (3.2.9) or (3.2.10) leads to the relation

$$\frac{D_1}{\sin\phi} + \frac{D_2}{\cos\phi} = 0, \tag{3.2.13}$$

or AO = OB in Figure 3.4. Therefore the electric displacement $\boldsymbol{D}$ oscillates along AB, which is one of the two axes of the section under consideration. The second allowed direction of oscillation of $\boldsymbol{D}$ is parallel to X_3, from equation (3.2.7).

Among the various central sections of the indicatrix, circular sections have special meaning. Depending on the crystal symmetry, the indicatrix can be a triaxial ellipsoid, an ellipsoid of rotation, or a sphere, having therefore two, one, or an infinite number of circular sections respectively. Each circular section determines a plane of optical isotropy for the crystal, within which the refractive index has the same value in any direction. The normal to such a plane is called an *optic axis*. Any beam of radiation whose normal $\boldsymbol{l}$ is parallel to an optic axis does not suffer double refraction and emerges from the crystal undeviated from its original direction for any state of linear polarization. These properties allow crystals to be divided into biaxial, uniaxial and isotropic classes respectively. We shall not treat this classification in any more detail, as it is dealt with in various of the monographs already referred to. We shall, however, analyse in more detail the path of a beam of polarized radiation passing through an anisotropic medium, which is of importance in selecting and interpreting optical measurements.

Consider therefore the crystal plate shown in Figure 3.5, which is supposed to have been cut from a monoclinic crystal along the (001) crystallographic plane. This case is sufficiently simple to allow relatively straightforward analysis but sufficiently complicated to allow relatively straightforward generalization to other crystal systems and other crystallographic planes. The plate is cut by two optical planes π_1 and π_2, both perpendicular to (001). The plane π_1 contains the crystallographic $\boldsymbol{a}$ and $\boldsymbol{c}$ axes and principal refractive indices n_1 and n_3. The plane π_2 is determined by the unique crystallographic axis $\boldsymbol{b}$, along which n_2 lies, and the normal to the plate, x_3. The remaining axes x_1 and x_2 are determined by the intersections of π_1 and π_2 with the plate, as shown in the figure. Finally, the angle ϕ relates the directions of x_1 and the principal refractive index n_1; it fixes the orientation of the indicatrix axes relative to the crystallographic axes in the crystal (010) plane.

Now assume that a plane polarized electromagnetic wave strikes the plate at normal incidence; the frequency of the wave is taken to be sufficiently far from any absorptions so that the crystal is transparent. If $\boldsymbol{l}$ is the unit vector parallel to the electrical displacement $\boldsymbol{D}$, then the components of $\boldsymbol{D}$ in the principal axis system are (Dl_1, Dl_2, Dl_3). Since $\boldsymbol{D}$ suffers no discontinuity

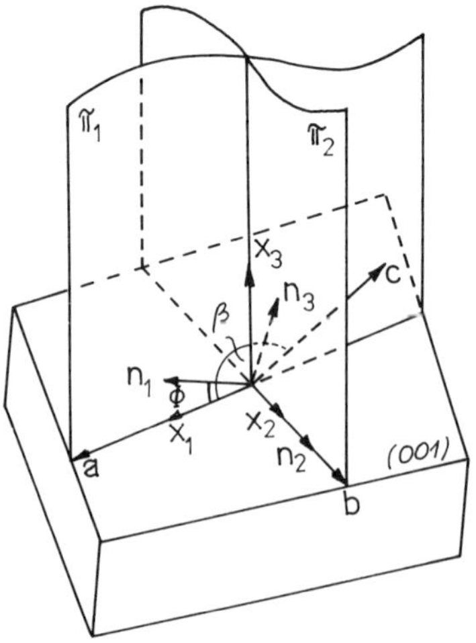

Figure 3.5. Allowed polarization states of a wave travelling through a (001) plate. Directions a, x_1, n_1, x_3, n_3 and c all lie in one plane, π_1

across the boundary between air and the crystal, these components refer both to air and to the crystal. However, the components of $\boldsymbol{E}$ change from (El_1, El_2, El_3) in the air to $(Dl_1/\varepsilon_0\varepsilon_1, Dl_2/\varepsilon_0\varepsilon_2, Dl_3/\varepsilon_0\varepsilon_3)$ inside the crystal. It follows that $\boldsymbol{D}$ and $\boldsymbol{E}$ make an angle ξ inside the crystal instead of being parallel as outside it: see Figure 3.6. The angle ξ is determined by

$$\cos\,\xi = \frac{\boldsymbol{D}\cdot\boldsymbol{E}}{|\boldsymbol{D}\,\|\,\boldsymbol{E}|} \tag{3.2.14}$$

$$= \frac{\sum_{i=1} (l_i^2/\varepsilon_0\varepsilon_i)}{\left\{\sum_{i=1} (l_i^2/\varepsilon_0^2\varepsilon_i^2)\right\}^{1/2}} \tag{3.2.15}$$

$$= \frac{\sum_{i=1} (l_i/n_i)^2}{\left\{\sum_{i=1} (l_i/n_i^2)^2\right\}^{1/2}}\,. \tag{3.2.16}$$

The same angle is made between the ray direction in the crystal and the negative x_3 axis, so that a knowledge of the three principal refractive indices n_i and of the direction of $\boldsymbol{D}$ allows us to find the deviation of the beam in the crystal from its direction of incidence. In most cases here we will be interested in simple situations, usually with normal incidence.

In general, birefringence will cause the incident beam to divide into two beams inside the crystal. If we wish to avoid this complication we have to choose one of two special orientations of $\boldsymbol{D}$. With reference to Figure 3.6, these are the following.

(1) $\boldsymbol{l} = (\cos\phi, 0, -\sin\phi)$, or $\boldsymbol{D} \parallel x_1$. Using this form of $\boldsymbol{l}$ in equation (3.2.16) we find by differentiation that the maximum deviation occurs for $\phi = 45^\circ$, when

$$\cos\,\xi_{\max} = \frac{1/n_1^2 + 1/n_2^2}{2\{1/n_1^4 + 1/n_2^4\}^{1/2}} \tag{3.2.17}$$

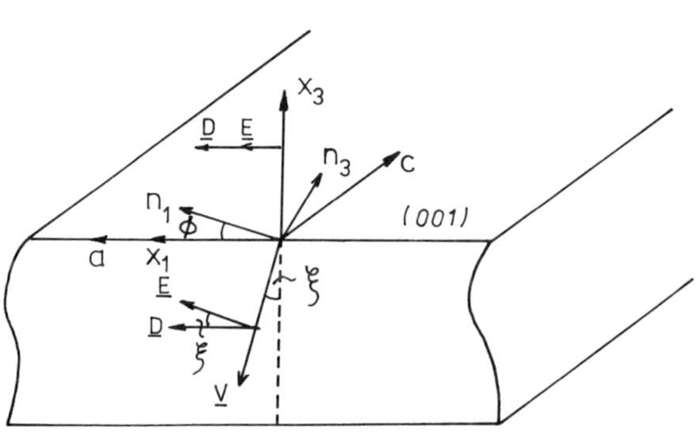

Figure 3.6. Orientations of the vectors $\boldsymbol{D}$ and $\boldsymbol{E}$ of a wave in a (001) crystal plate

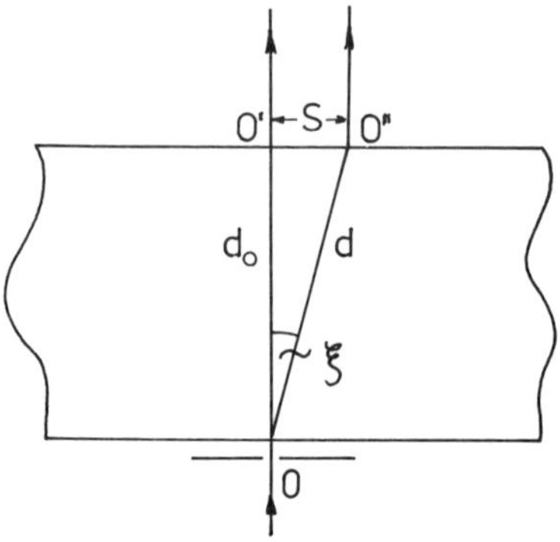

Figure 3.7. Displacement S of the emerging ray O″ after passing through a birefringent plate of thickness d_0

Assuming $n_1 = 1.5$ and $n_2 = 2.0$, for example, we obtain $\xi_{max} = 15.6°$. Thus in most cases met experimentally, where ϕ differs from the optimum 45° and the birefringence is modest, the angle ξ will not exceed a few degrees. However, ξ can be significant in certain cases, and ignoring it in the spectroscopy of crystals can even lead to misinterpretation of the polarizations of absorption bands.

(2) $\boldsymbol{l} = (0, 1, 0)$ or $\boldsymbol{D} \parallel x_2$. In this case $\cos \xi = 1$ so that $\xi = 0$. This result has a more general application: if the vector $\boldsymbol{D}$ is parallel to one of the three principal axes of the indicatrix, there is no deviation of the light beam.

The angular deviation of the light beam can be observed in a simple experiment as illustrated in Figure 3.7 [7]. A crystal plate in a polarizing microscope is illuminated by a narrow beam of polarized radiation coming from the underside of the plate through a small hole O in an opaque foil. In the 45° position of the crystal, two images of O, O′ and O″, will be observed with equal intensities. Denoting the distance between them by S, we see that

$$\tan \xi = \frac{S}{d_0} \tag{3.2.18}$$

where d_0 is the thickness of the plate; as both S and d_0 can be measured, the angle ξ can be determined experimentally. Note also that the path length for the beam passing through the crystal is not d_0 but d, where

$$d = d_0/\cos \xi. \tag{3.2.19}$$

3.3 MEASUREMENT OF BIREFRINGENCE

The birefringence of a crystal plate is the difference between the largest and smallest values of the refractive index in the plane of the plate. This in turn is the difference between the semi-axes of the elliptical central section made by the plane of the plate with the indicatrix ellipsoid. In the simplest case when the plate is cut perpendicular to the direction of one of the principal refractive indices n_k, the birefringence B_{ij} is just the difference between the other two principal refractive indices:

$$B_{ij} = n_i - n_j. \tag{3.3.1}$$

So defined, B_{ij} can have either sign, but experiments usually determine only $|B_{ij}|$. To find the sign of B_{ij}, separate methods must be used, as described in monographs dealing with applications of the polarizing microscope [8]. From each crystal, plates can be prepared with birefringences increasing from zero to values limited by n_i, n_j and n_k.

Birefringence is of interest in its own right rather than just as a difference of separately measurable refractive indices for various reasons. In particular, rather simple experimental methods are available to measure a difference of refractive indices to considerably higher accuracy than that obtainable in conventional methods for measuring individual refractive indices. As a result, birefringence measurements serve to give valuable information about the medium under investigation. An immediate example is the detection of circular birefringence (optical activity) as a component of the total birefringence. Circular birefringence occurs when left-hand circularly polarized light travels through the crystal with a different velocity from right-hand circularly polarized light incident in an identical manner, and also serves to rotate the plane of linearly polarized light [9]. The precision available in birefringence measurements also means that they can reveal small changes in the optical properties of the material caused by changes in temperature or pressure, including the effects of subtle phase transitions.

The birefringence also determines the difference in optical path length, Γ_{ij}, the retardation τ and the phase difference ϕ between two light beams entering the crystal. As we already know, a beam incident parallel to the principal direction of ε_k with the electric vector oscillating along the direction of ε_i moves with a velocity different from that when the oscillation is along the direction of ε_j. If the thickness of the crystal is d, the optical path length difference between the beams is

$$\Gamma_{ij} = (n_i - n_j)d = B_{ij}d. \tag{3.3.2}$$

A beam incident parallel to the direction of ε_k with an arbitrary polarization will generate both these beams simultaneously at the crystal surface, but by the time they emerge from the crystal they will differ by a retardation τ such that

$$\tau = \frac{d}{v_i} - \frac{d}{v_j} = \frac{d(n_i - n_j)}{c} = \frac{B_{ij}d}{c} \tag{3.3.3}$$

where c is the speed of light *in vacuo*. By the same token, the beams will differ in phase by an angle ϕ such that

$$\phi = 2\pi\left\{\frac{d}{\lambda_i} - \frac{d}{\lambda_j}\right\} = 2\pi\,\frac{B_{ij}d}{\lambda_0} \qquad (3.3.4)$$

where λ_0 is the wavelength of the radiation *in vacuo*. These definitions and relations will be needed for discussing the measurement techniques which follow.

The simplest way to measure B_{ij}, though not a very accurate one, is the interference method shown in Figure 3.8a. The birefringent crystal plate K is placed with one principal direction lying at 45° between the easy directions of crossed polarizers P and A. Monochromatic radiation of controllable wavelength λ is incident on the polarizer. In a suitable range of λ, depending on the birefringence and the sample thickness d, the retardation between the beams allows them to interfere when brought to the same oscillation direction by the analyser. The intensity of the beam emerging from A is therefore a periodic function of λ as shown in Figure 3.8b. The interference maxima occur for wavelengths where the optical path difference Γ_{ij} is an even number of half wavelengths, i.e. a whole number of wavelengths, whence

$$B_{ij}d = m\lambda \qquad (m = 1, 2, \ldots). \qquad (3.3.5)$$

Measurements are conveniently made as a function not of wavelength λ but of wavenumber $\tilde{\nu} = 1/\lambda$, and then successive maxima occur at wavenumbers

$$\tilde{\nu}_m = \frac{m}{B_{ij}d}. \qquad (3.3.6)$$

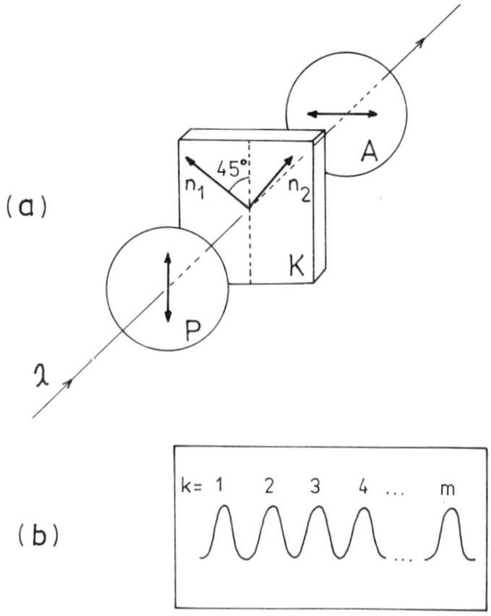

Figure 3.8. An interference method (a) of measuring the birefringence of a crystal plate from the separation of the interference fringes (b)

Knowledge of the absolute value of m, the order of interference, is not essential provided successive maxima can be identified, because $\tilde{\nu}_m$ varies linearly with a slope B_{ij}^{-1} whatever the starting point for counting m. However, some departure from a linear dependence can occur if the crystal has a strong optical absorption near the wavelengths studied, because the refractive index then becomes a complex quantity.

It frequently happens that the birefringence of a given crystal plate is too small or too large to allow experiments at convenient wavelengths. In this case, it is possible to use an additional birefringent plate and measure the sum or difference of the two birefringences. The first case was described by Wardzyński [10] as an aid for measuring very small birefringences induced in crystals by mechanical stress. The second case [11] is shown schematically in Figure 3.9. The sample of thickness d_s is assembled with another birefringent plate of thickness d_c using a drop of suitable immersion medium. The optical planes of the system are aligned so that the slow direction in one crystal is parallel to the fast direction in the other. The birefringence of the composite system shown in Figure 3.9 is then

$$B = \frac{(\omega d_c + n_2 d_s) - (\varepsilon' d_c + n_1 d_s)}{d_c + d_s}. \quad (3.3.7)$$

There will also be a special case in which the thickness of the auxiliary plate d_c^0 will lead to vanishing birefringence:

$$d_c^0 = \frac{n_1 - n_2}{\omega - \varepsilon'} d_s. \quad (3.3.8)$$

The auxiliary plate is conveniently cut from calcite, and the notation used for the refractive indices corresponds to ω being the refractive index for the ordinary ray and ε' that for the extraordinary ray. Calcite has the advantage that its principal refractive indices vary only weakly with temperature: for $\lambda = 656.3$ nm

$$\omega_t = 1.6544 + 0.19 \times 10^{-5}\, t/^{\circ}\mathrm{C} \quad (3.3.9)$$

$$\varepsilon_t = 1.4846 + 1.18 \times 10^{-5}\, t/^{\circ}\mathrm{C}. \quad (3.3.10)$$

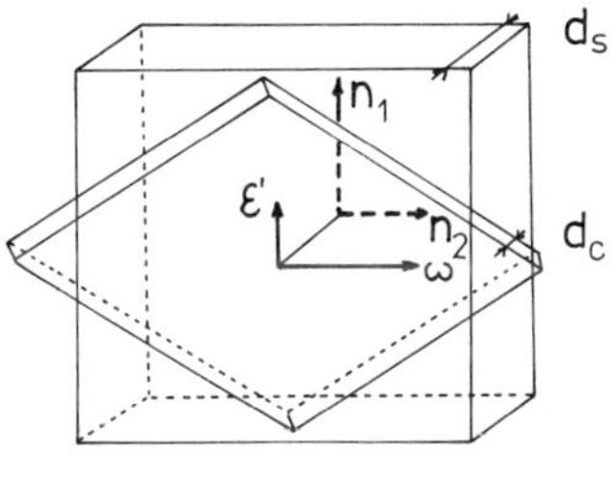

Figure 3.9. Optical compensation used to diminish the birefringence of a crystal sample

For a calcite plate limited by the natural cleavage, the refractive indices are ω_t and ε_t', where

$$\varepsilon_t' = \left\{\frac{\cos^2\phi}{\varepsilon_t^2} + \frac{\sin^2\phi}{\omega_t^2}\right\}^{-1/2} \tag{3.3.11}$$

and $\phi = 45.38^\circ$ is the angle made by the trigonal axis with the cleavage plane. Combining these equations we obtain the refractive index ε_t' in the cleavage plane as

$$\varepsilon_t' = 1.5638 + 0.76_2 \times 10^{-5}\ t/^\circ\text{C}. \tag{3.3.12}$$

More advanced methods of measuring birefringence depend on a more detailed treatment of the state of polarization of an electromagnetic wave. This is conveniently achieved through the graphical representation by means of *Poincaré's sphere* [12]. The general state of polarization of an electromagnetic wave is specified by an ellipse described by the electric displacement vector $\boldsymbol{D}$ in the XY plane, in a clockwise (negative) or anticlockwise (positive) sense as for an observer looking towards the light source; the light propagates in the Z direction perpendicular to the plane of the paper (see Figure 3.10a). The major axis of the ellipse makes an angle ψ with the X axis, and the ellipticity of the wave is described by the angle ω such that $\tan\omega = b/a$, where b and a are the semi-minor and semi-major axes. For $\omega = 0$ we have a plane polarized wave, and for $|\omega| = \pi/4$ we have circular polarization.

The representation of this state using Poincaré's sphere is illustrated in Figure 3.10b. The state is specified by the point P on the surface of a sphere of unit radius. The angle 2ψ is the latitude of P, and 2ω is its longitude. Plane polarized states therefore lie on the equator. These include in particular the plane polarized states X and Y vibrating along the coordinate axes, which are seen to be diametrically opposed. Similarly any pair of points at opposite ends of a diameter represent orthogonal states of polarization. The remaining two pure states $\omega = \pm\pi/4$ correspond to left- and right-hand circularly polarized radiation, and are represented by poles labelled L and R.

The particular advantage of the Poincaré sphere is that it permits the representation not only of the state of polarization of a light wave but also of the birefringence of a crystal plate. As we have seen, a non-absorbing plate can transmit two orthogonally polarized waves without changing their state of polarization, these waves corresponding to the principal axes of the appropriate central section of the indicatrix. On the Poincaré sphere, these states of a plate which has, in general, an elliptical birefringence, are specified by the points M and N (see Figure 3.11a) at opposite ends of a diameter. A wave of polarization M or N passes through the crystal with unchanged polarization, but an arbitrary wave of polarization P will be resolved in the crystal into two waves of polarization M and N. It then emerges from the crystal with polarization Q.

The polarization state Q can be determined as follows. The sphere is rotated about the axis MN by the angle Δ' which is the phase difference between M

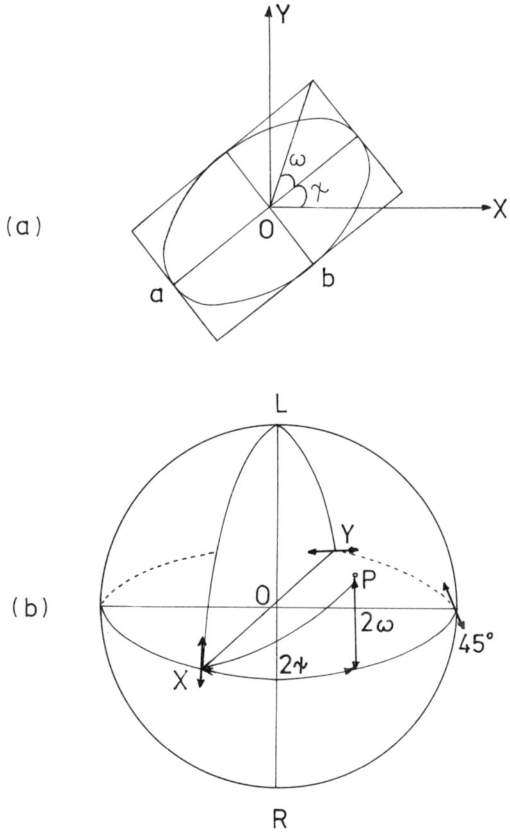

Figure 3.10. General state of polarization of a wave (a) and its representation on the Poincaré sphere (b)

and N components of the vibration P when they reach the back surface of the crystal plate (having been in phase at that surface). The rotation of the spherical surface is clockwise about the point representing the faster state (here M), for an observer looking from outside towards the centre of the sphere, as shown in the Figure 3.11a; it is anticlockwise when looking along the direction NO. Then Q is the point into which the original polarization state P is rotated. There are also some special cases. If the birefringence of the plate corresponds to a pure linear polarizations X and Y (X being the faster ray) with a phase difference δ', then the rotation axis of the sphere will be XY, thus rotating P to the point Q' representing the emergent state of polarization. If the birefringence of the plate corresponds to pure circular polarizations of phase difference ρ', the rotation axis of the sphere is LR but the rotation is $2\rho'$. This yields the transmitted ray Q'', which has the same ellipticity as P (same latitude) but the longer axis of the ellipse has been

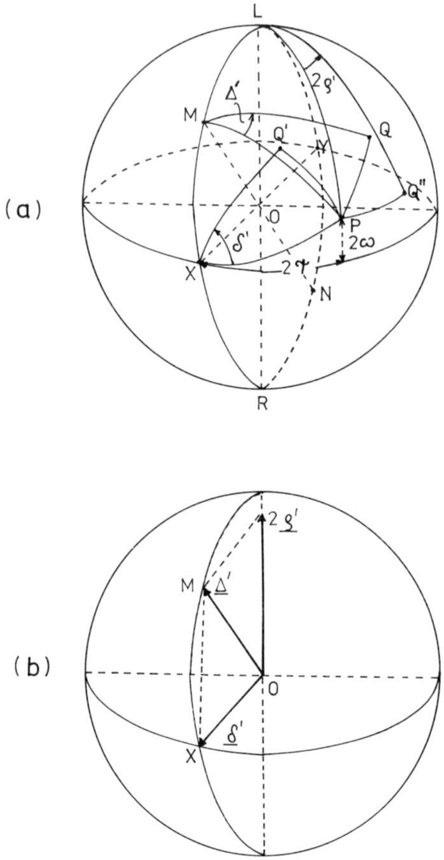

Figure 3.11. Various types of birefringence (a) and the additivity rule (b)

rotated by ρ'. Thus a linearly polarized beam may emerge from the plate either linearly or elliptically polarized, depending on the state of polarization of the incident beam and the properties of the crystal plate.

General elliptical birefringence of a crystal plate is composed of linear and circular contributions. For a very thin plate, the phase differences Δ', δ' and $2\rho'$ combine as vectors corresponding to infinitesimal rotations as illustrated in Figure 3.11b, where

$$\boldsymbol{\Delta}' = \boldsymbol{\delta}' + 2\boldsymbol{\rho}'. \tag{3.3.13}$$

Then from equation (3.3.4) the birefringence for a plate of thickness d will be

$$B = \frac{\lambda_0}{2\pi} (\boldsymbol{\Delta}' \cdot \boldsymbol{\Delta}')^{1/2}/d^2 \tag{3.3.14}$$

$$= \frac{\lambda_0}{2\pi} (\delta^2 + 4\rho^2)^{1/2} \qquad (3.3.15)$$

where $\delta = \delta'/d$ and $\rho = \rho'/d$ are the phase differences per unit length and λ_0 is the vacuum wavelength. Hence the application of the Poincaré sphere gives us a simple method to determine the state of polarization of the emerging beam or to analyse the optical properties of the plate when the polarizations of the incident and emergent beams are known.

A particular application of Poincaré's sphere allows birefringence to be determined from the polarization of the radiation scattered on structural imperfections in a crystal, whether natural or artificial. Apart from weak inelastic Brillouin or Raman scattering from lattice vibrations [13], ideal crystals do not scatter radiation, unlike liquids or gases. Real crystals show elastic scattering owing to departures from ideal periodicity such as regions of imperfect stoichiometry, foreign inclusions, dislocations or ferroelectric or magnetic domains. If the dimensions of such centres are smaller than the wavelength of the incident radiation, Rayleigh elastic scattering takes place. Analysis of the state of polarization of the scattered radiation then provides information on the nature, size and spatial distribution of the scattering centres if the deviations from ideality are substantial, or on the nature and magnitude of the birefringence if the deviations from ideality are small [12]. It is the latter case with which we shall be concerned here. The sample has the form of a parallelepiped with imperfections introduced by fine scratches on the face through which the scattered radiation is to be observed. In addition, this face should be slightly ground to make a small angle with the direction of the incident beam so as to obtain uniform illumination of the scattering centres, as shown in Figure 3.12.

The scattering centres serve as local indicators of the phase in the incident radiation as a function of penetration depth in the crystal. Partial beams scattered in all directions can interfere with one another, so that the observer looking at the roughened face at an angle Θ from the direction of incidence sees a system of interference fringes of separation Λ. Therefore Θ is the scattering angle and ψ the azimuth of $\boldsymbol{E}$ in the scattered beam with respect to the plane of observation π_1 (Figure 3.12). The conditions for interference are closely related to those met in an optical wedge cut from the same crystal in the same orientation. If the angle of the wedge is α, the separation Λ_w between fringes in the wedge experiment is related to Λ by [12]

$$\Lambda_w = \Lambda \cot \alpha. \qquad (3.3.16)$$

The simplest geometry is met for a scattering angle $\Theta = 90^\circ$: in this case the component of $\boldsymbol{E}$ in the plane π_1 must vanish for any ψ. In this geometry the propagation direction and the vibration direction of the scattered beam lie in a plane perpendicular to the incident beam in the crystal. The two polarization states of the scattered beam revealed by the analyser A placed in front of

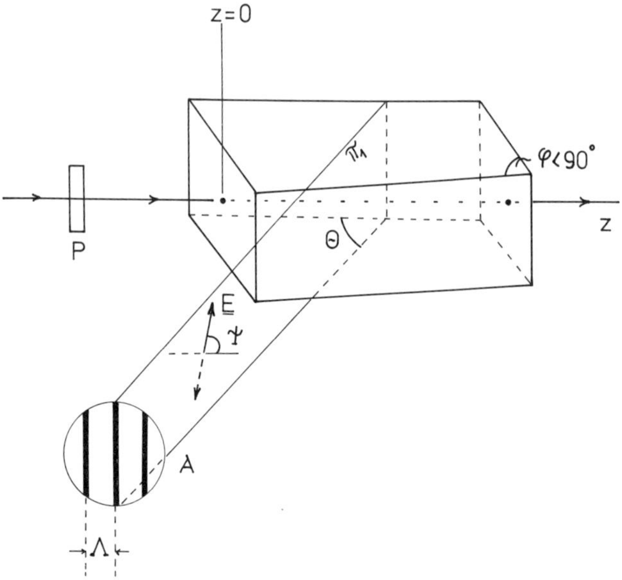

Figure 3.12. Verreault's method of birefringence measurement

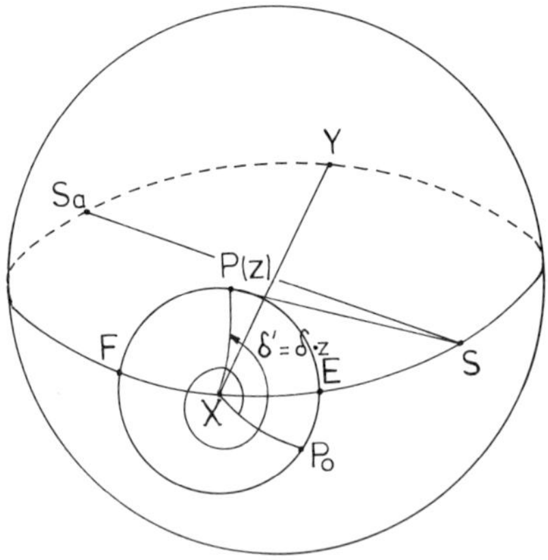

Figure 3.13. Geometry of scattering on small centres

the scattering face and perpendicular to π_1 can be described by orthogonal polarization states S and S_a on the Poincaré sphere.

We will restrict further consideration to a crystal showing only linear birefringence and to linear polarization of the incident beam. For such a case the Poincaré sphere is shown in Figure 3.13. Let z be an axis parallel to the propagation direction in the crystal, and let the incident beam in the initial polarization state P_0 strike the crystal at $z = 0$ (see Figure 3.12). The polarization states along $z > 0$ are then distributed in such a way that the point P which represents them moves in a circle centred on X (where as before X and Y represent the pure linear polarizations of the plate, X being the faster ray).

The intensity of the scattered beam for propagation along z is given by the function

$$I = kI_0 \sin^2(\tfrac{1}{2} PS) \tag{3.3.17}$$

where PS is the length of the arc of the great circle passing through S and $P(z)$. The intensity is therefore a periodic function of z with minima appearing when $P(z)$ coincides with the point E and maxima when $P(z)$ coincides with the point F in Figure 3.13. In general, the interference fringes are separated by a distance

$$\Lambda = \frac{2\pi}{\Delta} = \frac{2\pi}{(\delta^2 + 4\rho^2)^{1/2}} \tag{3.3.18}$$

and the dark fringes occur at positions

$$z_n = \left(n + \frac{P_0E}{2\pi}\right)\Lambda \tag{3.3.19}$$

where $n = 0, 1, 2, \ldots$ In the case illustrated by Figure 3.13, $\rho = 0$ and $P_0E = 0$, so that the positions z_n of the interference fringes and the crystal thickness d immediately give the value of the linear birefringence δ. Use of a quarter-wave plate also allows the sign of the birefringence to be determined from the direction in which the whole interference system is moved when the plate is inserted.

This method can be used with a precision of 1% or better in the range

$$10^{-6} < (n_i - n_k) < 0.2. \tag{3.3.20}$$

For example, Verreault [12] measured the birefringence of quartz at 632.8 nm and 27 °C to be

$$n_e - n_\omega = (8.99 \pm 0.05) \times 10^{-3} \tag{3.3.21}$$

$$\rho = (18.76 \pm 0.05)\ \text{degree mm}^{-1}. \tag{3.3.22}$$

Another method of measuring the linear birefringence which is equivalent in sensitivity to Verreault's method uses a Sénarmont quarter-wave compensator [14]. This requires simpler instrumentation and can be particularly useful for measuring the temperature dependence of birefringence of very thin crystalline samples. However, the samples have to be of very good optical quality: cleaved or polished samples are not normally sufficiently transparent or uniform in thickness or both. Excellent results are obtained on plates containing suitable natural faces of the sort which frequently occur in crystal growth from organic substances by sublimation. Very small plates can be studied using the polarizing microscope.

The experimental arrangement is shown schematically in Figure 3.14. Approximately monochromatic radiation in a parallel beam produced by the

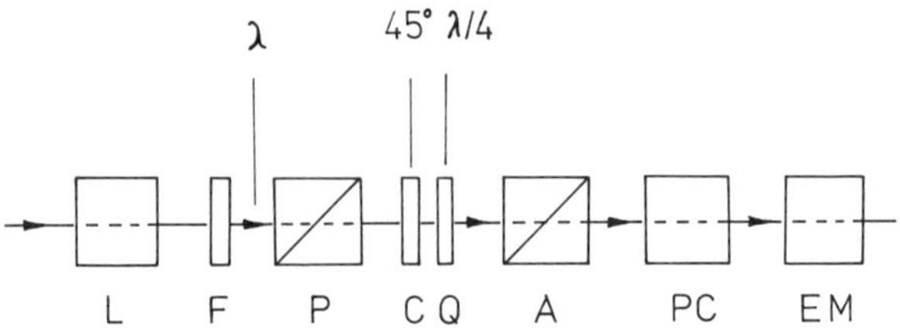

Figure 3.14. Compensation method of birefringence measurements

lamp L (e.g. a mercury lamp) and the interference filter F is linearly polarized after passing through the polarizer P. The sample C is placed in the 45° position midway between the fast and slow axes. The quarter-wave plate Q restores the radiation emerging from the plate, which is generally elliptically polarized, to a state of linear polarization. The azimuth of the ellipse describing the ellipticity of the emerging beam can be determined from the angle of rotation of the analyser A which yields complete extinction. Compensation is achieved when no current flows through the vacuum photocell PC as detected by the electrometer EM. Highest accuracy results when the quarter-wave plate is exactly matched to the wavelength of the monochromatic radiation used. For this reason it is advisable to prepare the plate by cleaving gypsum crystal to the required thickness in the laboratory.

The path difference (3.3.2) can be expressed as

$$\Gamma = (m + k)\lambda \tag{3.3.23}$$

where $m = 0, 1, 2, \ldots$ and $0 \leqslant k \leqslant 1$. By means of the compensation method we can measure only the fractional wavelength contribution $k\lambda$, with an accuracy of ± 1.5 nm. The integral wavelength contribution $m\lambda$ must be determined separately, for example using an interference polarizing microscope. Because the integral part can be determined accurately and the fractional part with only a small error, the overall accuracy will depend mainly on the accuracy with which the crystal thickness can be determined (which is one reason why a highly uniform thickness is necessary).

3.4 APPROXIMATE TREATMENTS OF LOCAL FIELD

We now turn to the microscopic interpretation of the optical properties of molecular crystals in terms of the molecular polarizability. The link between the macroscopic and microscopic properties is provided by the induced polarization $\boldsymbol{P}$. It is related to the macroscopic electric field $\boldsymbol{E}$ appearing in Maxwell's equations for the crystal by

$$\boldsymbol{P} = \varepsilon_0 \boldsymbol{\chi} \cdot \boldsymbol{E} \tag{3.4.1}$$

$$= \varepsilon_0 (\boldsymbol{\epsilon} - \boldsymbol{1}) \cdot \boldsymbol{E} \tag{3.4.2}$$

where $\boldsymbol{\chi}$ is the electric susceptibility tensor and $\boldsymbol{\epsilon}$ is the relative permittivity tensor. We exclude non-linear effects for the time being, so that $\boldsymbol{\epsilon}$ is independent of $\boldsymbol{E}$. For non-magnetic media of unit relative permeability μ, the principal components of $\boldsymbol{\epsilon}$ are the squares of the principal refractive indices, n_i^2, so that the macroscopic optical properties determine the relationship between $\boldsymbol{P}$ and $\boldsymbol{E}$.

At the same time, $\boldsymbol{P}$ is the induced dipole moment per unit volume in a uniform crystal. We saw earlier that the crystal properties depend on the contents of the crystallographic unit cell. If this contains Z molecules labelled k with induced dipole moments $\boldsymbol{p}_k$ in a volume v, then

$$\boldsymbol{P} = \sum_{k=1}^{Z} \boldsymbol{p}_k / v. \tag{3.4.3}$$

The induced dipole moments are in turn given by the molecular polarizabilities $\boldsymbol{\alpha}_k$ as

$$\boldsymbol{p}_k = \boldsymbol{\alpha}_k \cdot \boldsymbol{F}_k. \tag{3.4.4}$$

Here $\boldsymbol{F}_k$ is the *local field* or polarizing field, which is determined not only by the externally applied field (e.g. that of an incident light wave) but also by the fields of the surrounding polarized molecules. In the magnetic case we had $\mu \approx 1$ so that the magnetization $\boldsymbol{I}$ was much smaller than the magnetic field $\boldsymbol{H}$, with the result that local field effects were negligible. However, in the dielectric case we have values of ε of typically 3 for molecular crystals, so that $\boldsymbol{P}/\varepsilon_0$ is typically twice as large as $\boldsymbol{E}$, and local field effects are very important. Thus the essential step in providing a molecular interpretation of the optical properties is to relate the local fields $\boldsymbol{F}_k$ to $\boldsymbol{E}$. Once this is done, $\boldsymbol{P}$ can be related to $\boldsymbol{E}$ via equations (3.4.3) and (3.4.4) and this relationship is then compared with (3.4.2) to yield $\boldsymbol{\epsilon}$ in terms of the $\boldsymbol{\alpha}_k$. We note at once that if the molecules have zero polarizability, the refractive index is unity as in a vacuum.

The foregoing gives the basis for both the approximate treatments to be presented in this subsection and the rigorous molecular theories to be presented in the following subsection. In particular, it separates the microscopic molecular response determined by the polarizability from the collective response of the molecules which determines the local field. Before proceeding to the calculation of the local field, we consider these separate aspects in a little more detail.

The properties of a molecule inside a crystal are modified by its interaction with surrounding molecules. In particular, the polarizability is dominated by the outermost electrons least tightly bound to the nuclear framework, and these will clearly be affected by the surrounding molecular charge distributions. A molecule in a crystal is therefore characterized by an *effective polarizability* which differs from the free polarizability. As the dispersion, overlap and exchange interactions are all of short range, the difference between the free and effective polarizabilities is dominated by the interaction with nearest neighbours. In particular, a molecule may occupy a site of lower symmetry in the crystal than the free-molecule symmetry or may adopt a different configuration, in which case the effective polarizability must differ from the free polarizability.

As the effective polarizability differs from the free polarizability, so the effective polarizability will differ for the same molecule in different crystalline phases, and indeed in the same phase at different temperatures, given that the observed properties represent some thermal average over the anisotropic molecular motion. However, differences in effective polarizability may be rather small provided the molecular packing is similar in the different phases. This will often be the case in molecular crystals, where phase transitions may involve only subtle changes of orientation. It is therefore frequently convenient and reasonable to assume that differences in optical properties in different crystal phases, and changes in the same phase at different temperatures, arise only from changes in the orientation and separation of molecules and not from changes in their effective polarizability. Similarly one may assume that crystallographically inequivalent molecules of the same chemical species in a crystal have the same effective polarizability, an example being tetracene, where the environments of the inequivalent molecules differ little from one another or from the single molecular environment in the very similar crystal of anthracene. Nevertheless, the assumption of an invariant effective polarizability should not be made uncritically, especially where the chemical environment changes, for instance in the different charge-transfer crystals based on anthracene as donor.

Turning now to the local field, we note that the outline treatment given above implies the existence of a local field at a molecule, i.e. at a point. A point-molecule algebra is common and convenient, but requires some justification and interpretation. In general, polarizability response is non-local: the polarization at one point is determined by the local field not only at that point but also at all other points. However, translational symmetry allows a polarizability and a local field characteristic of a single unit cell to be defined [15], and recognition of the highly localized nature of the electronic wavefunction within a suitably defined molecular volume allows these definitions to be extended to give a polarizability and a local field characteristic of a single molecule in terms of averages over the molecular volume [16]. Thus in equations (3.4.3) and (3.4.4) k is indeed a label for a molecule rather than the position of some representative point in the molecule.

Approximate theories of the local field usually imply some generalization of the Lorenz–Lorentz equation. The local field is written as

$$\boldsymbol{F} = \boldsymbol{E} + \boldsymbol{E}_{\mathrm{p}} + \boldsymbol{E}_{\mathrm{d}} \tag{3.4.5}$$

where $\boldsymbol{E}$ is the macroscopic electric field; $\boldsymbol{E}_{\mathrm{p}}$ is the field due to the polarization charges on a spherical surface centred on a particular molecule, the crystal being treated as a dielectric continuum outside this surface; and $\boldsymbol{E}_{\mathrm{d}}$ is the field at the molecule due to the other discrete molecules inside the spherical surface.

The field $\boldsymbol{E}_{\mathrm{p}}$ was calculated by Lorentz for an isotropic medium as

$$\boldsymbol{E}_{\mathrm{p}} = \frac{1}{3\varepsilon_0} \boldsymbol{P} \tag{3.4.6}$$

where $\boldsymbol{P}$ is the polarization (see for example [2] or [9]). The field $\boldsymbol{E}_{\mathrm{d}}$ is determined by the induced dipole moments of the discrete molecules and the dipole tensor; in a cubic solid or an isotropic medium the dipole tensor averages to zero, and then

$$\boldsymbol{F} = \boldsymbol{E} + \frac{1}{3\varepsilon_0} \boldsymbol{P}. \tag{3.4.7}$$

In such media, the relative permittivity tensor reduces to a scalar, so that

$$\begin{aligned} \boldsymbol{P} &= \varepsilon_0(\varepsilon - 1)\boldsymbol{E} \\ &= \varepsilon_0 \chi \boldsymbol{E}. \end{aligned} \tag{3.4.8}$$

Substitution in (3.4.7) then yields the *Lorentz local field*:

$$\begin{aligned} \boldsymbol{F} &= \tfrac{1}{3}(\varepsilon + 2)\boldsymbol{E} \\ &= (1 + \tfrac{1}{3}\chi)\boldsymbol{E}. \end{aligned} \tag{3.4.9}$$

With a suitable average polarizability α, the induced dipole moment is given by $\boldsymbol{p} = \alpha\boldsymbol{F}$, so that the polarization becomes

$$\boldsymbol{P} = \frac{N}{V} \boldsymbol{p} = \frac{N\alpha}{3V} (\varepsilon + 2)\boldsymbol{E} \tag{3.4.10}$$

where N is the number of molecules in volume V. Comparison with equation (3.4.8) yields

$$\varepsilon_0(\varepsilon - 1) = \frac{N\alpha}{3V} (\varepsilon + 2). \tag{3.4.11}$$

This is conventionally rearranged into the *Clausius–Mossotti equation*

$$P_{\mathrm{m}} \equiv \frac{\varepsilon - 1}{\varepsilon + 2} \frac{M}{\rho} = \frac{L\alpha}{3\varepsilon_0}. \tag{3.4.12}$$

Here P_{m} is the *molar polarization*, M is the molar mass, ρ is the density, and L is the Avogadro constant. The right-hand side of (3.4.12) contains only universal constants and the molecular property α, so that P_{m} is a combination of macroscopic quantities which should be constant. Complications due to the tendency of molecules with permanent dipole moments to align in an electric field are ignored. The molar polarization is found to be essentially constant in gases, but deviations from constancy may occur in liquids and especially solids if the averaging implicit in α changes, apart from any change from the free polarizability to an effective polarizability in these condensed phases.

At optical frequencies, molecular orientation by the electric vector of the radiation can be neglected. Further neglecting magnetic effects, we have $\varepsilon = n^2$, where n is the mean refractive index. Substitution in (3.4.12) then yields the *Lorenz–Lorentz equation* for the *molar refraction*:

$$R_{\mathrm{m}} \equiv \frac{n^2-1}{n^2+2}\frac{M}{\rho} = \frac{L\alpha}{3\varepsilon_0}. \tag{3.4.13}$$

In a molecular crystal the number of molecules per unit volume is conveniently replaced according to

$$\frac{N}{V} = \frac{L\rho}{M} = \frac{Z}{v} \tag{3.4.14}$$

where Z is the number of molecules per unit cell and v is the volume of the unit cell. The mean polarizability of the unit cell Γ is similarly given by $Z\alpha$, so that (3.4.14) can be rearranged into

$$\frac{n^2-1}{n^2+2} = \frac{\Gamma}{3\varepsilon_0 v}. \tag{3.4.15}$$

The generalization to anistropic crystals made by Rousset [17] corresponds to the assumption that an equation of the form (3.4.15) holds for each principal direction i of the indicatrix, so that

$$\frac{n_i^2-1}{n_i^2+2} = \frac{\Gamma_i}{3\varepsilon_0 v} \qquad (i = 1, 2, 3). \tag{3.4.16}$$

This is equivalent to the assumption that the Lorentz local field (3.4.9) can be generalized in a similar way:

$$F_i = \tfrac{1}{3}(n_i^2+2)E_i \qquad (i = 1, 2, 3). \tag{3.4.17}$$

In this formalism, the principal axes of the indicatrix and of the unit-cell polarizability tensor $\mathbf{\Gamma}$ coincide. Because $\mathbf{\Gamma}$ is characteristic of the unit cell as a whole, it is in some senses still a macroscopic quantity. However, it can be related to the molecular polarizability tensor $\boldsymbol{\alpha}$ by applying the oriented-gas model (cf. equations (1.6.5) and (1.6.6)):

$$\mathbf{\Gamma} = \boldsymbol{g}\cdot\left\{\sum_{k=i}^{Z} \boldsymbol{c}^{(k)\mathrm{T}}\cdot\boldsymbol{\alpha}\cdot\boldsymbol{c}^{(k)}\right\}\cdot\boldsymbol{g}^{\mathrm{T}} \tag{3.4.18}$$

Here the matrix $\boldsymbol{c}^{(k)}$ relates the principal axes of the molecular polarizability of molecule k to the crystal axes. The summation extends over all molecules in the unit cell; if there are sets of molecules in the unit cell which are not crystallographically equivalent, then $\mathbf{\Gamma}$ consists of a number of independent sums, one for each set of molecules. The matrix $\boldsymbol{g}$ brings the unit-cell polarizability in the crystal axes to its principal axes, coinciding with the principal axes of the indicatrix because of (3.4.16).

According to equation (3.4.17), the local field is determined only by macroscopic factors, namely the principal components and principal axes of $\boldsymbol{\epsilon}$. The microscopic structure of the crystal appears only in the unit-cell polarizability $\mathbf{\Gamma}$ given by (3.4.18), which does not affect the local field directly. For this reason, numerical values obtained from (3.4.16) and (3.4.18) should be treated with some caution. These equations provide a universally applicable method of analysing the refractive indices which is very useful in interpreting changes such as the influence of temperature or pressure on optical properties. However, the numerical results should not necessarily be regarded as having any physical significance beyond that of parameters in a model used for interpolation.

Although the present approach gives the unit-cell polarizability, it does not give the molecular polarizability $\boldsymbol{\alpha}$ directly. The problem of inverting equation (3.4.18) hinges on determining the principal axes of $\boldsymbol{\alpha}$, and can be treated in the same way as in determining the molecular susceptibility $\boldsymbol{K}$ from the crystal magnetic susceptibility $\boldsymbol{x}$ as outlined in Section 2.5. If the free molecule belongs to a point group of symmetry C_{2h} or higher, the principal axes of $\boldsymbol{\alpha}$ are identical with the molecular axes of symmetry L, M, N, and we may invoke the assumption that the same principal axes apply in the crystal. For less symmetrical molecules, we could try to find the principal axes by adding component tensors for the molecular framework and its substituents assuming some suitable invariance between related crystals, but this does not appear to have been done systematically in the case of polarizability. In general, approximations cannot be avoided except for one molecule per unit cell of triclinic symmetry, unless the molecules share an element of the crystal symmetry.

Setting aside these reservations, we now illustrate how equations (3.4.16) and (3.4.18) are applied. In Table 3.1 are given complete optical data for several aromatic hydrocarbon crystals, from the monograph of Winchell [18]. Here n_2 is set parallel to the crystallographic $\boldsymbol{b}$ axis, and n_1 and n_3 lie in the (010) or ac plane; ϕ is the angle between n_1 and the crystallographic $\boldsymbol{a}$ axis. Our aim will be to deduce a molecular polarizability $\boldsymbol{\alpha}$ compatible with the n_i and to calculate the angle ϕ_{calc}. We start from the polarizabilities $\boldsymbol{\alpha}^{(0)}$ for the free molecule obtained using the anisotropic bond increments given by Le Fèvre [19] (see Table 3.2). The aromatic rings are treated as regular hexagons, with the CH_2 groups in fluorene adopting a regular tetrahedral structure.

The problem is solved by the method of successive approximations. First $\boldsymbol{\Gamma}^{(0)}$ is calculated in the crystal $\boldsymbol{abc}^*$ axes. For example, for naphthalene we

Table 3.1 Experimental values of the refractive indices of aromatic hydrocarbon crystals at $\lambda = 546$ nm [18]

Crystal	n_1	n_2	n_3	ϕ	ϕ_{calc}
Benzene	1.544	1.646	1.550	0	0
Naphthalene	1.525	1.722	1.945	42.3	22.6
Anthracene	1.556	1.786	1.959	26.9	27.1
Phenanthrene	1.548	1.920	1.724	27.0	26.7
Fluorene	1.578	1.919	1.663	0	0

Table 3.2 Polarizability increments for bonds, according to Le Fèvre [18]; b_l is the polarizability along the bond, b_t is the polarizability across the bond in the molecular plane, and b_v is the polarizability across the bond perpendicular to the molecular plane

	$b/10^{-40}$ F m^2		
Bond	b_l	b_t	b_v
C—H	0.71	0.71	0.71
C—C	1.10	0.30	0.30
C_{ar}—C_{ar}	2.49	0.23	0.66
C—Cl	4.68	2.15	1.65

Note that a polarizability volume of 1×10^{-24} cm^3 (the customary unit in cgs–esu) corresponds to a polarizability of 1.1119×10^{-40} F m^2 (the SI unit).

have

$$\boldsymbol{\Gamma}^{(0)} = \sum_{k=1}^{2} \boldsymbol{c}^{(k)\mathrm{T}} \cdot \boldsymbol{\alpha}^{(0)} \cdot \boldsymbol{c}^{(k)} \tag{3.4.19}$$

$$= 2\sum_{A} \begin{pmatrix} c_{A1}^2 \alpha_A^{(0)} & 0 & c_{A1}c_{A3}\alpha_A^{(0)} \\ 0 & c_{A2}^2 \alpha_A^{(0)} & 0 \\ c_{A3}c_{A1}\alpha_A^{(0)} & 0 & c_{A3}^2 \alpha_A^{(0)} \end{pmatrix} \tag{3.4.20}$$

where the summation extends over the principal axes $A = L, M, N$ of the molecule and $\boldsymbol{c}$ gives the orientation of the axes in the $\boldsymbol{abc}^*$ system. Then $\boldsymbol{\Gamma}^{(0)}$ is transformed to its principal axes by means of the matrix

$$\boldsymbol{g} = \begin{pmatrix} \cos\phi_0 & 0 & \sin\phi_0 \\ 0 & 1 & 0 \\ -\sin\phi_0 & 0 & \cos\phi_0 \end{pmatrix} \tag{3.4.21}$$

where the angle of rotation in the ac plane is

$$\phi_0 = \tfrac{1}{2}\tan^{-1} \frac{2\Gamma_{13}^{(0)}}{\Gamma_{11}^{(0)} - \Gamma_{33}^{(0)}}. \tag{3.4.22}$$

Writing

$$q_i = \frac{n_i^2 - 1}{n_i^2 + 2} = \frac{\Gamma_{ii}}{3\varepsilon_0 v} \tag{3.4.23}$$

where for the monoclinic system

$$v = abc \sin\beta \tag{3.4.24}$$

we obtain the zeroth approximation for the refractive indices:

$$n_i^{(0)} = \left(\frac{1 + 2q_i^{(0)}}{1 - 2q_i^{(0)}}\right)^{1/2}. \tag{3.4.25}$$

For the next approximation the experimental refractive indices and ϕ_0 are used as the starting point to calculate $\mathbf{\Gamma}^{(1)}$, $\boldsymbol{\alpha}^{(1)}$ and ϕ_1. This procedure is repeated with the experimental direction cosines $\boldsymbol{c}$ and the refractive indices n_i until convergence is reached. The first three approximations are shown in Table 3.3 for naphthalene and the isostructural anthracene crystal. For the complete set of crystals the final results are shown in Table 3.4 together with values derived for the free molecules from the polarizability increments in

Table 3.3 Calculations of molecular polarizability by the method of successive approximations

	$\alpha/10^{-40}$ F m^2						
Order	L	M	N	n_1	n_2	n_3	ϕ
A. Naphthalene							
(0)	21.8	19.6	12.9	1.508_3	1.660_2	1.871_0	22.24
(1)	23.2	20.1	13.2	1.522_8	1.722_0	1.948_4	22.62
(2)	23.1	20.1	13.3	1.525_0	1.722_0	1.945_0	22.62
		Experiment		1.525	1.722	1.945	
B. Anthracene							
(0)	31.1	26.7	17.6	1.522_4	1.726_2	1.976_7	27.68
(1)	30.6	28.4	18.6	1.560_6	1.786_0	1.952_6	27.12
(2)	30.7	28.4	18.4	1.555_9	1.786_0	1.959_3	27.14
		Experiment		1.556	1.786	1.959	

Table 3.4 Polarizability of selected molecules calculated in the crystal and from the increments in Table 3.2

		Polarizability/10^{-40} F m^2		
Molecule	State	α_L	α_M	α_N
Benzene	Free	12.5	12.5	8.2
	Crystal	12.5	11.8	9.3
Naphthalene	Free	21.8	19.6	12.9
	Crystal	23.1	20.1	13.3
Anthracene	Free	31.1	26.7	17.6
	Crystal	30.7	28.5	18.5
Phenanthrene	Free	30.0	27.8	17.6
	Crystal	33.4	38.7	5.1
Fluorene	Free	27.6	25.6	16.5
	Crystal	28.9	24.6	18.7

Table 3.2. We see that except for phenanthrene the components of $\boldsymbol{\alpha}$ derived for the crystal do not differ greatly from those derived from the increments. The latter, described as those for the free molecule, are in fact calculated from measurements of the electro-optic Kerr effect in solution [19]. It appears clear that α_N for phenanthrene is too low and α_M too high. This may be due to the fact that phenanthrene has a permanent dipole moment (although so too does fluorene), or perhaps to some effect in the crystal, which is known to have a subtle and poorly understood phase transition.

A further example is the gypsum crystal, $CaSO_4 \cdot 2H_2O$. Though not strictly a molecular crystal, it provides a good illustration of how the method of Rousset can be used with judicious approximations to relate the optical anisotropy of a crystal to the polarizability anisotropy of its constituents. Neutron diffraction [20] shows the structure to belong to the monoclinic space group $I2/a$. The unit cell has $a = 5.68$, $b = 15.18$, $c = 6.52$ Å and $\beta = 118.4°$, with $Z = 4$ formula units. The Ca^{2+} and SO_4^{2-} ions occupy sites of C_2 symmetry, but for the $SO_4{}^{2-}$ ions deviations from the free T_d symmetry are small, so that we can assume that both ions retain effectively isotropic polarizability in the crystal. The oxygen atoms in the water molecules occupy general positions, with the hydrogen atoms belonging to two symmetrically independent sets also in general positions, so that the two bond lengths $O-H_1$ and $O-H_2$ in a water molecule are slightly different.

Examination of the optical properties shows that the water molecules play an essential role in determining the anisotropy. The principal refractive indices for $\lambda = 589$ nm are $n_1 = 1.5299$, $n_2 = 1.5230$ and $n_3 = 1.5207$ [21], where as before $n_2 \parallel \boldsymbol{b}$. It is found that the principal axes of the indicatrix in the (010) plane lie essentially parallel or perpendicular to the O—H directions in that plane [22], Figure 3.15. We will assume that this fact is significant, and use it to deduce $\boldsymbol{\alpha}$ for the water molecules and the sum of the isotropic

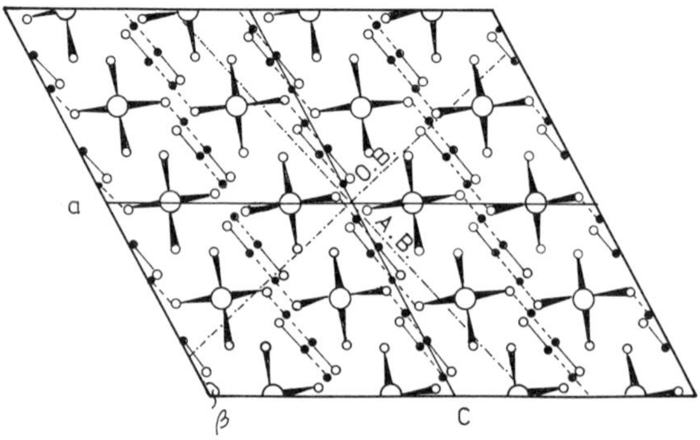

Figure 3.15. Projection of the gypsum structure on the (010) plane, showing the principal axes in the plane

Ca^{2+} and $SO_4{}^{2-}$ polarizabilities by the method of successive approximations.

We start from the free polarizability $\boldsymbol{\alpha}^{(0)}$ calculated by Liebmann and Moskowitz [23], which in the molecular axis system gives $\alpha_L = 1.836$, $\alpha_M = 1.363$, $\alpha_N = 1.614 \times 10^{-40}\ \mathrm{F\,m^2}$, with a mean polarizability $\langle\alpha\rangle = 1.604 \times 10^{-40}\ \mathrm{F\,m^2}$. Then in the optical axis system the unit-cell polarizability in the zeroth approximation is given by $\boldsymbol{\Gamma}^{(0)} = 8(1.730, 1.380, 1.705) \times 10^{-40}\ \mathrm{F\,m^2}$, as there are eight water molecules in the unit cell. If $N_i^{(0)}$ denotes the zeroth-order approximation to the contribution of the water molecules to the refractive index n_i and $\Delta_i^{(0)}$ denotes the contribution of the ions, then

$$\Delta_i^{(0)} = n_i - N_i^{(0)}. \tag{3.4.26}$$

The process of successive approximations will be considered to have converged in kth order when $\Delta_i^{(k)}$ is the same for all i so that the contribution of the ions is isotropic. Starting from $\boldsymbol{\Gamma}^{(0)}$ we obtain $\Delta_1^{(0)} = 0.3266$, $\Delta_2^{(0)} = 0.3554$, $\Delta_3^{(0)} = 0.3176$, already quite close to isotropy. For the next approximation we use the mean value $\langle\Delta^{(0)}\rangle = 0.3332$, and obtain the isotropic result $\Delta_1^{(1)} = \Delta_2^{(1)} = \Delta_3^{(1)} \equiv \Delta = 0.3319$, which terminates the procedure. Solution of three inhomogeneous equations derived from (3.4.18) then gives the water polarizabilities as $\alpha_L = 1.598$, $\alpha_M = 1.592$, $\alpha_N = 1.619 \times 10^{-40}\ \mathrm{F\,m^2}$, with a mean polarizability $\langle\alpha\rangle = 1.603 \times 10^{-40}\ \mathrm{F\,m^2}$. The anisotropy is small—much smaller than in the free molecule—and this is consistent with the small birefringence of gypsum.

To obtain α^{iso}, the isotropic polarizability of the ions, we average equation (3.4.23) writing $n_i = N_i + \Delta$ in the numerator, and then ascribe all terms dependent on Δ to α^{iso}. The result is

$$\frac{2\Delta\langle N\rangle + \Delta^2}{\langle n^2\rangle + 2} = \frac{4\alpha^{\text{iso}}}{3\varepsilon_0 v} \tag{3.4.27}$$

where the factor 4 comes from the number of ion pairs in the unit cell of volume $v = 123.65\ \text{Å}^3$. Then we obtain $\alpha^{\text{iso}} = 6.85 \times 10^{-40}\ \mathrm{F\,m^2}$. There are no values derived directly from experiment to allow a comparison with this value. However, if we take a polarizability for Ca^{2+} calculated from the correction term in the spectroscopic Rydberg–Ritz series of $0.63 \times 10^{-40}\ \mathrm{F\,m^2}$ [24], and one for $SO_4{}^{2-}$ of $4.23 \times 10^{-40}\ \mathrm{F\,m^2}$ obtained from density and refractive index measurements on sodium sulphate solutions [25], we find $\alpha^{\text{iso}} = 4.87 \times 10^{-40}\ \mathrm{F\,m^2}$. In view of the various sources of data used in these calculations, the agreement between the values of α^{iso} is not unsatisfactory.

These examples show that using Rousset's formalism with the oriented gas model provides a tractable method for interpreting the optical properties of crystals which leads to reasonable conclusions.

An alternative approach to the relation between n and $\boldsymbol{\alpha}$ has been presented by Lasheen and co-workers [26, 27]. By combining (3.4.13) and

Table 3.5 Structural and optical constants of molecular crystals

Compound	Summary formula and macroscopic data	Structural data	Refractive indices (λ_D, Na)		Refraction: Crystal	Refraction: Molecule
A. Orthorhombic crystals						
1. Triphenylbenzene	$(C_6H_5)_3C_6H_3$ $M = 306.14$ $\rho = 1237$ $V/Z = 410.9$	$Pna2_1$ [28] $a = 7.47$ $b = 19.66$ $c = 11.19$ $Z = 4$	$n_x = 1.5241$ $n_y = 1.8670$ $n_z = 1.8725$ [18]	$n_a = 1.509$ $n_b = 1.843$ $n_c = 1.849$ [26]	$R_a = 73.9$ $R_b = 109.9$ $R_c = 110.5$ [26]	$r_L = 28.2$ $r_M = 28.9$ $r_N = 16.7$ [26]
2. Acenaphthene	$C_{10}H_6(CH_2)_2$ $M = 154.21$ $\rho = 1190$ $V/Z = 209.6$	$Pcm2_1$ [29] $a = 8.290$ $b = 14.000$ $c = 7.225$ $Z = 4$	$\alpha = 1.4065$ $\beta = 1.4678$ $\gamma = 1.6201$ [30]	$n_a = 1.489$ $n_b = 1.642$ $n_c = 1.396$ [26]	$R_a = 37.4$ $R_b = 46.8$ $R_c = 31.1$ [26]	$r_L = 11.7$ $r_M = 12.0$ $r_N = 5.1$ [26]
3. Sodium hydrogen phthalate	$C_6H_4(COOH) \cdot (COONa)$ $M = 188.13$ $\rho = 1504$ $V/Z = 207.8$	$B2ab$ [31] $a = 6.76$ $b = 9.31$ $c = 26.42$ $Z = 8$	$n_x = 1.485$ $n_y = 1.661$ $n_z = 1.668$ [18]	$n_a = 1.476$ $n_b = 1.665$ $n_c = 1.678$ [26]	$R_a = 70.6$ $R_b = 92.8$ $R_c = 97.4$ [26]	$r_L = 12.4$ $r_M = 11.8$ $r_N = 8.1$ [26]
4. Potassium hydrogen phthalate	$C_6H_4(COOH) \cdot (COOK)$ $M = 204.22$ $\rho = 1579$ $V/Z = 214.7$	$P2_1ab$ [32] $a = 6.46$ $b = 9.60$ $c = 13.85$ $Z = 4$	$n_x = 1.498$ $n_y = 1.659$ $n_z = 1.663$ [18]	$n_a = 1.494$ $n_b = 1.632$ $n_c = 1.674$ [26]	$R_a = 37.6$ $R_b = 46.1$ $R_c = 48.5$ [26]	$r_L = 12.8$ $r_M = 12.1$ $r_N = 8.3$ [26]
5. *m*-Dinitrobenzene	$C_6H_4(NO_2)_2$ $M = 168.05$ $\rho = 1593$ $V/Z = 175.2$	$Pbn2_1$ [33] $a = 13.20$ $b = 13.97$ $c = 3.80$ $Z = 4$	$n_x = 1.432$ $n_y = 1.765$ $n_z = 1.839$ [18]	$n_a = 1.746$ $n_b = 1.841$ $n_c = 1.482$ [26]	$R_a = 42.8$ $R_b = 46.8$ $R_c = 30.1$ [26]	$r_L = 12.4$ $r_M = 10.6$ $r_N = 7.0$ [26]

6. Acetanilide	$C_6H_5NHCOCH_3$ $M = 135.04$ $\rho = 1206$ $V/Z = 185.8$	$Pbca$ [34] $a = 19.640$ $b = 9.483$ $c = 7.979$ $Z = 8$	$n_x = 1.515$ $n_y = 1.620$ $n_z = 1.733$ [18]	$n_a = 1.748$ $n_b = 1.612$ $n_c = 1.524$ [26]	$R_a = 45.5$ $R_b = 38.9$ $R_c = 34.3$ [26]	$r_L = 5.8$ $r_M = 5.5$ $r_N = 3.6$ [26]
7. Anthranilic acid	$C_6H_4(NH_2)_2 \cdot (COOH)$ $M = 137.1$ $\rho = 1420$ $V/Z = 160.3$	$Pcn2$ [35] $a = 12.83$ $b = 10.77$ $c = 9.28$ $Z = 8$	$n_x = 1.560$ $n_y = 1.730$ $n_z = 1.760$ [18]	$n_a = 1.508$ $n_b = 1.768$ $n_c = 1.736$ [26]	$R_a = 28.8$ $R_b = 40.0$ $R_c = 38.8$ [26]	$r_L = 5.1$ $r_M = 5.2$ $r_N = 3.2$ [26]
8. *N*-Bromosuccinimide	$C_4H_4O_2NCl$ $M = 133.54$ $\rho = 1650$ $V/Z = 133.2$	$P2_12_12_1$ [36] $a = 6.41$ $b = 7.11$ $c = 11.69$ $Z = 4$		$n_a = 1.668(3)$ $n_b = 1.616(3)$ $n_c = 1.661(4)$ [27]	$R_a = 30.9(2)$ $R_b = 28.3(2)$ $R_c = 29.9(3)$ [27]	$r_L = 7.4(3)$ $r_M = 8.1(4)$ $r_N = 6.8(2)$ [27]
9. *N*-Bromosuccinimide	$C_4H_4O_2NBr$ $M = 178.00$ $\rho = 2109$ $V/Z = 139.3$	$P2_12_12_1$ [36] $a = 6.48$ $b = 7.25$ $c = 11.86$ $Z = 4$		$n_a = 1.706(3)$ $n_b = 1.641(2)$ $n_c = 1.681(3)$ [27]	$R_a = 32.8(2)$ $R_b = 30.4(2)$ $R_c = 31.9(2)$ [27]	$r_L = 7.9(2)$ $r_M = 8.5(4)$ $r_N = 7.4(1)$ [27]
10. Ammonium hydrogen-*d*-tartrate	$C_4H_4O_6(NH_4) \cdot H$ $M = 167.07$ $\rho = 1680$ $V/Z = 165.94$	$P2_12_12_1$ [37] $a = 7.648$ $b = 11.066$ $c = 7.843$ $Z = 4$		$n_a = 1.534(1)$ $n_b = 1.500(2)$ $n_c = 1.510(2)$ [27]	$R_a = 30.9(1)$ $R_b = 29.2(2)$ $R_c = 29.7(2)$ [27]	$r_L = 7.4(1)$ $r_M = 8.0(1)$ $r_N = 7.1(2)$ [27]
11. Potassium hydrogen-*d*-tartrate	$C_4H_4O_6K \cdot H$ $M = 188.18$ $\rho = 1954$ $V/Z = 157.20$	$P2_12_12_1$ [37] $a = 7.64$ $b = 10.62$ $c = 7.75$ $Z = 4$		$n_a = 1.566(2)$ $n_b = 1.534(2)$ $n_c = 1.544(2)$ [27]	$R_a = 31.4(2)$ $R_b = 29.9(3)$ $R_c = 30.4(2)$ [27]	$r_L = 7.5(5)$ $r_M = 8.0(1)$ $r_N = 7.3(1)$ [27]

(continued)

Table 3.5 *(continued)*

Compound	Summary formula and macroscopic data	Structural data	Refractive indices (λ_D, Na)		Refraction: Crystal	Refraction: Molecule
B. Monoclinic crystals						
12. Anthracene	$C_{14}H_{10}$ $M = 178.2$ $\rho = 1028$ $V/Z = 237.08$ $Z = 2$	$P2_1/a$ [38] $a = 8.561$ $b = 6.035$ $c = 9.163$ $\beta = 124.70^\circ$	$n_x = 1.556$ $n_y = 1.786$ $n_z = 1.959$ [18]	$n_1 = 1.959$ $n_2 = 1.485$ $n_3 = 1.837$ [26]	$R_1 = 84.4$ $R_2 = 49.8$ $R_3 = 76.7$ [26]	$r_L = 42.3$ $r_M = 42.5$ $r_N = 20.8$ [26]
13. Biphenyl	$C_{12}H_{10}$ $M = 154.2$ $\rho = 1224$ $V/Z = 221.4$ $Z = 2$	$P2_1/a$ [39] $a = 8.63$ $b = 5.63$ $c = 9.15$ $\beta = 95.1^\circ$	$n_x = 1.561$ $n_y = 1.658$ $n_z = 1.945$ [18]	$n_1 = 1.945$ $n_2 = 1.550$ $n_3 = 1.661$ [26]	$R_1 = 60.6$ $R_2 = 40.1$ $R_3 = 46.6$ [26]	$r_L = 31.1$ $r_M = 26.9$ $r_N = 15.6$ [26]
14. Hexachlorobenzene	C_6Cl_6 $M = 284.74$ $\rho = 1816$ $V/Z = 232.0$ $Z = 2$	$P2_1/c$ [40] $a = 8.08$ $b = 3.87$ $c = 16.65$ $\beta = 117.0^\circ$	$n_1 = 1.738$ $n_2 = 1.701$ $n_3 = 1.601$ [26]		$R_1 = 63.1$ $R_2 = 60.7$ $R_3 = 53.7$ [26]	$r_L = 31.4$ $r_M = 31.4$ $r_N = 26.1$ [28]
15. *p*-Dichlorobenzene	$C_6H_4Cl_2$ $M = 146.95$ $\rho = 1526$ $V/Z = 157.1$ $Z = 2$	$P2_1/a$ [41] $a = 14.80$ $b = 5.78$ $c = 3.99$ $\beta = 113^\circ$	$n_1 = 1.752$ $n_2 = 1.528$ $n_3 = 1.679$ [26]		$R_1 = 39.3$ $R_2 = 29.6$ $R_3 = 36.4$ [26]	$r_L = 19.2$ $r_M = 20.3$ $r_N = 13.2$ [26]
16. Anthraquinone	$C_{14}H_8O_2$ $M = 208.20$ $\rho = 1438$ $V/Z = 239.1$	$P2_1/a$ [42] $a = 15.810$ $b = 3.942$ $c = 7.865$	$n_x = 1.506$ $n_y = 1.698$ $n_z = 1.816$ [18]	$n_1 = 1.875(3)$ $n_2 = 1.717(3)$ $n_3 = 1.486(2)$ [27]	$R_1 = 66.0(4)$ $R_2 = 57.0(4)$ $R_3 = 41.6(3)$ [27]	$r_L = 38(10)$ $r_M = 29(8)$ $r_N = 16.30(2)$ [27]

17. Tetrachloro-*p*-benzoquinone (chloranil)	$C_6Cl_4O_2$ $M = 245.89$ $\rho = 1712$ $V/Z = 207.4$ $Z = 2$	$P2_1/a$ [43] $a = 8.708$ $b = 5.755$ $c = 8.603$ $\beta = 105.85^\circ$		$n_1 = 1.522(2)$ $n_2 = 1.621(3)$ $n_3 = 1.589(2)$ [27]	$R_1 = 43.8(3)$ $R_2 = 50.5(4)$ $R_3 = 48.4(3)$ [27]	$r_L = 26(3)$ $r_M = 25.2(8)$ $r_N = 20(1)$ [27]
18. Tetrachloro-hydroquinone	$C_6Cl_4(OH)_2$ $M = 247.90$ $\rho = 2002$ $V/Z = 205.6$ $Z = 2$	$P2_1/c$ [44] $a = 8.214$ $b = 4.843$ $c = 12.441$ $\beta = 123.82^\circ$		$n_1 = 1.676(3)$ $n_2 = 1.625(2)$ $n_3 = 1.636(3)$ [27]	$R_1 = 46.6(3)$ $R_2 = 43.8(2)$ $R_3 = 44.4(4)$ [27]	$r_L = 22.8(22)$ $r_M = 26(2)$ $r_N = 20(1)$ [27]
19. *p*-Nitroaniline	$C_6H_4(NO_2) \cdot NH_2$ $M = 138.12$ $\rho = 1437$ $V/Z = 160.8$ $Z = 4$	$P2_1/n$ [45] $a = 12.336$ $b = 6.07$ $c = 8.592$ $\beta = 91.46^\circ$		$n_1 = 1.788(4)$ $n_2 = 1.525(2)$ $n_3 = 1.756(3)$ [27]	$R_1 = 40.6(4)$ $R_2 = 29.5(2)$ $R_3 = 39.4(3)$ [27]	$r_L = 9.6$ $r_M = 10.6$ $r_N = 7.1$ [27]
20. Isatine	$C_8H_5O_2N$ $M = 147.05$ $\rho = 1527$ $V/Z = 159.9$ $Z = 4$	$P2_1/c$ [46] $a = 6.19$ $b = 14.46$ $c = 7.17$ $\beta = 94.82^\circ$	$n_x = 1.460(5)$ $n_y = 1.80(3)$ $n_z = 1.90(3)$ [18]	$n_1 = 1.886(5)$ $n_2 = 1.453(2)$ $n_3 = 1.782(4)$ [27]	$R_1 = 44.3(5)$ $R_2 = 26.0(2)$ $R_3 = 40.5(4)$ [27]	$r_L = 10(2)$ $r_M = 11.0(7)$ $r_N = 6.60(1)$ [27]
21. Theophylline monohydrate	$C_5H_2O_2N_4 \cdot (CH_3)_2$ $M = 198.28$ $\rho = 1454$ $V/Z = 225.8$ $Z = 4$	$P2_1$ [47] $a = 13.3$ $b = 15.3$ $c = 4.5$ $\beta = 99.5^\circ$	$n_1 = 1.447$ $n_2 = 1.695$ $n_3 = 1.733$ [18]	$n_1 = 1.447(2)$ $n_2 = 1.687(4)$ $n_3 = 1.641(3)$ [27]	$R_1 = 36.4(2)$ $R_2 = 52.0(5)$ $R_3 = 49.2(4)$ [27]	$r_L = 13.0(1)$ $r_M = 12.4(20)$ $r_N = 9.1(8)$ [27]
22. 2,6-dimethyl-γ-pyrone	$C_7H_8O_2$ $M = 124.06$ $\rho = 1234$ $V/Z = 165.1$ $Z = 4$	$P2_1/c$ [48] $a = 7.672$ $b = 7.212$ $c = 13.92$ $\beta = 120.98^\circ$		$n_1 = 1.556(1)$ $n_2 = 1.463(1)$ $n_3 = 1.535(1)$ [27]	$R_1 = 32.32(9)$ $R_2 = 27.69(9)$ $R_3 = 31.30(9)$ [27]	$r_L = 8(2)$ $r_M = 8(2)$ $r_N = 6.3(0)$ [27]

(continued)

Table 3.5 *(continued)*

Compound	Summary formula and macroscopic data	Structural data	Refractive indices (λ_D, Na)	Refraction: Crystal	Refraction: Molecule
23. Parabanic acid	$CO(NH \cdot CO)_2$ $M = 114.03$ $\rho = 1713$ $V/Z = 110.5$ $Z = 4$	$P2_1/n$ [49] $a = 10.685$ $b = 8.194$ $c = 5.054$ $\beta = 92.73°$	$n_1 = 1.441(2)$ $n_2 = 1.554(3)$ $n_3 = 1.479(2)$ [27]	$R_1 = 17.6(1)$ $R_2 = 21.3(2)$ $R_3 = 18.9(1)$ [27]	$r_L = 6(2)$ $r_N = 4.4(1)$ $r_N = 4(2)$ [27]

M, molar mass, kg/mol; ρ, density, kg/m^3; V/Z, the volume per molecule in Å^3; a, b, c, unit cell parameters in Å; Z, number of molecules in the unit cell; n_x, n_y, n_z, refraction indices along the principal vibration directions; n_a, n_b, n_c, refractive indices along the crystallographic directions (orthorhombic system); n_1, n_2, n_3, refractive indices along the principal axes of dielectric tensor $\boldsymbol{\epsilon}$ (cf. text); R, refraction of the crystal; r, refraction of the molecule, each in cm^3/molecule.

(3.4.16) we can write the molar refraction of the crystal in terms of components R_i along the principal axes of the indicatrix given by

$$R = \frac{n_i^2 - 1}{n_i^2 + 2} \frac{M}{\rho} \tag{3.4.28}$$

Then molecular molar refractions r_A along the principal axes of the molecule are defined to satisfy

$$\sum_{i=1}^{3} R_i = Z \sum_{A=1}^{3} r_A \tag{3.4.29}$$

where it is usually assumed that R and r satisfy the oriented gas model (3.4.18).

Molecular refractions have been calculated from refractive indices measured at room temperature using the sodium D line, $\lambda_D = 589$ nm [26]. The results obtained by Lasheen and co-workers (adjusted to satisfy (3.4.29)) are shown in Table 3.5; note that small uncertainties in n may sometimes result in large errors in r. The convention used in constructing the table is that in orthorhombic crystals $R_a \parallel \boldsymbol{a}$, $R_b \parallel \boldsymbol{b}$ and $R_c \parallel \boldsymbol{c}$, while in monoclinic crystals $R_3 \parallel \boldsymbol{b}$ with R_1 and R_2 in the (010) or ac plane. The relation between polarizability and refraction is

$$\alpha_A = \frac{3}{M} \varepsilon_0 v \rho r_A \tag{3.4.30}$$

so that the r_A determine the α_A directly.

Lasheen and co-workers studied the relationship between the molecular refraction anisotropy Δr defined as

$$\Delta r = \tfrac{1}{2}(r_L + r_M) - r_N \tag{3.4.31}$$

and the corresponding molecular magnetizability anisotropy

$$\Delta K = \tfrac{1}{2}(K_L + K_M) - K_N. \tag{3.4.32}$$

They found a number of correlations. First, a strong magnetizability anisotropy was always accompanied by a strong polarizability anisotropy. Second, for planar molecules the highest magnetizability occurred normal to the plane while the lowest polarizability occurred in that direction. Third, the ratio $\Delta r/\Delta r_B$ between the refraction anisotropy and that of benzene, Δr_B, was always smaller than the corresponding ratio for the magnetizability anisotropy, $\Delta K/\Delta K_B$. This is attributable to the fact that the interactions between induced electric dipoles are much more important than those between induced magnetic dipoles. Finally, substituents usually reduce the optical anisotropy of aromatic molecules, depending on the nature and position of substitution.

3.5 RIGOROUS MOLECULAR THEORIES

The approximate treatments of the local field just described are convenient and yield plausible and useful results. However, they afford no fundamental understanding of the local field. We conclude our treatment of linear optical properties by describing rigorous molecular theories which relate the local field to the effective molecular polarizability in the crystal. This yields a relationship between the optical properties and the polarizability which shows, among other things, that a knowledge of the optical properties and the crystal structure does not usually suffice to determine the polarizability uniquely.

The basic concepts of the rigorous theory were introduced by Dunmur [50]. We consider a molecular crystal as consisting of Z interpenetrating sublattices labelled k, so that there are Z molecules in the primitive unit cell. Under the influence of the electric field $\boldsymbol{E}$ of an impinging electromagnetic wave, the molecules on sublattice k each acquire an induced dipole moment $\boldsymbol{p}_k$. Then the macroscopic polarization $\boldsymbol{P}$ is given by

$$\boldsymbol{P} = \sum_k \boldsymbol{p}_k / v \tag{3.5.1}$$

where the sum extends from $k = 1$ to Z and v is the unit-cell volume. The induced dipole moments are related to the corresponding local fields $\boldsymbol{F}_k$ by the effective polarizability $\boldsymbol{\alpha}_k$, so that

$$\boldsymbol{p}_k = \boldsymbol{\alpha}_k \cdot \boldsymbol{F}_k. \tag{3.5.2}$$

As before, there are no variables here which characterize the spatial extension of the molecules, so that the dipoles are treated as points (but see later for a more general treatment).

The electric field in the polarized crystal is a sum of the applied field and the fields of all the induced dipoles. Following a method introduced by Ewald [51, 52], it is possible to manipulate the induced dipole lattice sum so as to accelerate its convergence and furthermore to separate out the contribution from the macroscopic polarization and combine it with the applied field to give the macroscopic field $\boldsymbol{E}$ which appears in Maxwell's equations. The resulting expression for the local field is

$$\boldsymbol{F}_k = \boldsymbol{E} + \sum_{k'} \boldsymbol{L}_{kk'} \cdot \boldsymbol{p}_{k'} / \varepsilon_0 v. \tag{3.5.3}$$

Here $\boldsymbol{L}_{kk'}$ is a dimensionless *Lorentz-factor tensor* which depends only on the crystal structure. It is symmetric, and has a trace of unity,

$$\mathrm{Tr}\ \boldsymbol{L}_{kk} = 1 \tag{3.5.4}$$

and in order to be invariant under the point group of the unit cell it must satisfy

$$\boldsymbol{L}_{kk'} = \boldsymbol{L}_{k'k};\ \boldsymbol{L}_{kk} = \boldsymbol{L}_{k'k'}. \tag{3.5.5}$$

In the particular case of cubic symmetry the three diagonal elements of $\boldsymbol{L}$ must be equal, and because of (3.5.4) each must then equal 1/3. This factor is familiar from the approximate treatments: we now see that introducing $\boldsymbol{L}$

allows us to characterize properly the anisotropic way in which the sublattice polarizations contribute to the local field.

By substituting (3.5.2) in (3.5.3) we obtain a set of equations relating the local fields and the macroscopic field [53, 54]:

$$\boldsymbol{F}_k = \boldsymbol{E} + \sum_{k'} \boldsymbol{L}_{kk'} \cdot \boldsymbol{a}_{k'} \cdot \boldsymbol{F}_{k'} \tag{3.5.6}$$

where $\boldsymbol{a}_{k'} = \boldsymbol{\alpha}_{k'}/\varepsilon_0 v$ is a dimensionless reduced effective polarizability; in a three-dimensional system of units such as cgs–esu, we would have $a = 4\pi\alpha_{\text{cgs}}/v$. Rearrangement yields the set of equations

$$\sum_{k'} (\boldsymbol{1}\delta_{kk'} - \boldsymbol{L}_{kk'} \cdot \boldsymbol{a}_{k'}) \cdot \boldsymbol{F}_{k'} = \boldsymbol{E} \tag{3.5.7}$$

which demonstrate the proportionality between $\boldsymbol{F}$ and $\boldsymbol{E}$. The equations can be solved by introducing a $3Z \times 3Z$ matrix $\boldsymbol{S}$ with 3×3 submatrices

$$\boldsymbol{S}_{kk'} = \boldsymbol{1}\delta_{kk'} - \boldsymbol{L}_{kk'} \cdot \boldsymbol{a}_{k'} \tag{3.5.8}$$

a $3Z \times 1$ vector $\boldsymbol{F}$ with 3×1 subvectors $\boldsymbol{F}_k$, and a $3Z \times 3$ matrix $\boldsymbol{U}$ with 3×3 unit submatrices **1**. Then equation (3.5.7) becomes

$$\boldsymbol{S} \cdot \boldsymbol{F} = \boldsymbol{U} \cdot \boldsymbol{E} \tag{3.5.9}$$

with the solution

$$\begin{aligned} \boldsymbol{F} &= \boldsymbol{S}^{-1} \cdot \boldsymbol{U} \cdot \boldsymbol{E} \\ &= \boldsymbol{D} \cdot \boldsymbol{U} \cdot \boldsymbol{E} \end{aligned} \tag{3.5.10}$$

where for convenience we have introduced the $3Z \times 3Z$ matrix $\boldsymbol{D}$ equal to the inverse of $\boldsymbol{S}$. Then an individual local field is given by

$$\boldsymbol{F}_k = \sum_{k'} \boldsymbol{D}_{kk'} \cdot \boldsymbol{U}_{k'} \cdot \boldsymbol{E} \tag{3.5.11}$$

and since each submatrix $\boldsymbol{U}_{k'}$ is the unit 3×3 matrix we obtain

$$\boldsymbol{F}_k = \sum_{k'} \boldsymbol{D}_{kk'} \cdot \boldsymbol{E} \equiv \boldsymbol{d}_k \cdot \boldsymbol{E} \tag{3.5.12}$$

where $\boldsymbol{d}_k$ is the *local field tensor*.

Thus given the polarizabilities and the Lorentz-factor tensors one can calculate the local field tensor from a $3Z \times 3Z$ matrix inversion. Although the Lorentz-factor tensors and polarizability tensors are symmetric, their product is not, in general, and so the local field tensor is not symmetric. There is also nothing to require the local field tensor to be diagonal in the crystal axes or the principal optical axes as most approximate theories assume.

The crystal optical properties follow from equation (3.5.1) for the macroscopic polarization in terms of the sublattice dipole moments, which in turn are given in terms of the local fields by (3.5.2) and hence in terms of the macroscopic field with the help of (3.5.12), so that

$$\boldsymbol{P} = \sum_k \boldsymbol{\alpha}_k \cdot \boldsymbol{d}_k \cdot \boldsymbol{E}/v. \tag{3.5.13}$$

By comparison with the macroscopic expression $\boldsymbol{P} = \varepsilon_0 \boldsymbol{\chi} \boldsymbol{E}$ we find

$$\boldsymbol{\chi} = \sum_k \boldsymbol{a}_k \cdot \boldsymbol{d}_k. \tag{3.5.14}$$

Even with one molecule per unit cell the principal axes of $\boldsymbol{\chi}$ and $\boldsymbol{a}$ do not coincide, in general, because of the local field and its dependence on the Lorentz-factor tensor. Where there are several molecules per unit cell, the sublattice contributions to $\boldsymbol{\chi}$ will in general have terms allowed by the site symmetry but not by the crystal point group symmetry, so that the principal axes of $\boldsymbol{\chi}$ represent a yet more complicated resultant of different influences.

The direct influence of the Lorentz-factor tensor can also be shown by defining a $3Z \times 3Z$ matrix $\boldsymbol{A}$ with elements $\boldsymbol{A}_{kk'} = \boldsymbol{a}_k \delta_{kk'}$. Then

$$\boldsymbol{\chi} = \sum_{kk'} (\boldsymbol{A} \cdot \boldsymbol{D})_{kk'} \tag{3.5.15}$$

$$= \sum_{kk'} [(\boldsymbol{A}^{-1} - \boldsymbol{L})^{-1}]_{kk'}, \tag{3.5.16}$$

where $\boldsymbol{L}$ is the $3Z \times 3Z$ matrix with submatrices $\boldsymbol{L}_{kk'}$. It follows that $\boldsymbol{\chi}$ can be regarded as a sum of contributions $\boldsymbol{\chi}_{kk'}$ relating the polarization response at sublattice k to the macroscopic field stimulus at sublattice k'. This interpretation proves helpful in applications discussed later.

Given the microscopic expression (3.5.16) for the macroscopic optical susceptibility, we may seek to extract the effective polarizability from the susceptibility. For $Z = 1$ this is straightforward, leading to

$$\boldsymbol{a} = (\boldsymbol{\chi}^{-1} + \boldsymbol{L})^{-1} \equiv \boldsymbol{M}^{-1}. \tag{3.5.17}$$

In this case the site symmetry and the crystal point group symmetry must coincide, so that $\boldsymbol{\chi}$ and $\boldsymbol{L}$ have the same independent non-zero elements as $\boldsymbol{a}$, which is therefore determined uniquely.

For $Z > 1$, extracting a unique effective polarizability is possible only if the crystal structure constrains $\boldsymbol{a}$ to have no more independent non-zero elements than $\boldsymbol{\chi}$. In general the site symmetry is lower than the crystal point group symmetry, so that each $\boldsymbol{a}_k$ has more independent non-zero elements than $\boldsymbol{\chi}$, which cannot therefore suffice to determine the $\boldsymbol{a}_k$ completely [53–56]. Physically this difficulty can be seen to arise because $\boldsymbol{\chi}$ describes only the *sum* of the sublattice polarizations, by (3.5.1), whereas the $\boldsymbol{a}_k$ describe *individual* sublattice polarizations. Unless symmetry determines all the differences between the sublattice polarizations, $\boldsymbol{\chi}$ is insufficient to determine all the $\boldsymbol{a}_k$.

Various methods can be used to explore the constraints placed on the effective polarizability by the requirement that it should yield the observed susceptibility. One method starts with equation (3.5.6) for the local fields and eliminates the macroscopic field using

$$E = \chi^{-1} \cdot P/\varepsilon_0$$
$$= \chi^{-1} \sum_k a_k \cdot F_k, \qquad (3.5.18)$$

with the result

$$F_k = \sum_{k'} M_{kk'} \cdot a_{k'} \cdot F_{k'} \qquad (3.5.19)$$

where $M_{kk'} \equiv \chi^{-1} + L_{kk'}$. Treating F_k as $a_k^{-1} \cdot a_k \cdot F_k$, we have a set of homogeneous equations in the unknowns $a_k \cdot F_k$ to which the usual consistency condition can be applied. In the case $Z = 2$, elimination of $a_1 \cdot F_1$ shows that a solution with $a_2 \cdot F_2$ non-zero requires

$$a_1^{-1} = M_{11} + M_{12} \cdot (a_2^{-1} - M_{22})^{-1} \cdot M_{21}. \qquad (3.5.20)$$

In addition, if the molecules are crystallographically equivalent then their reduced polarizabilities can be obtained from that in the molecular axis a using

$$a_k = c_k \cdot a \cdot c_k^{\mathrm{T}} \qquad (3.5.21)$$

where c_k is the direction cosine matrix relating the crystal to the molecular axes. Solutions to equation (3.5.20) can be obtained by iteration given a suitable starting polarizability. For this purpose, the free-molecule polarizability represents a physically reasonable choice. One can then view the iteration procedure as a numerical representation of the process by which the molecule adapts to its surroundings in the crystal [55].

Solutions to equation (3.5.20) obtained iteratively for four hydrocarbon crystals [53] are shown in Table 3.6, while the resulting mean polarizabilities and polarizability anisotropies are shown in Table 3.7. As expected, both the mean polarizability and the anisotropy increase with the number of benzene rings, whether for the free molecule or for the molecule in the crystal, and irrespective of whether results are taken from Table 3.4 using approximate local fields or Table 3.6 using rigorous ones. However, the results from Table 3.6 are much further from the free molecule results than those from Table 3.4. To some extent this is not surprising: the 'free molecule' results are obtained by extrapolations to infinite dilution from solution measurements using Lorentz local field corrections which are somewhat generalized to obtain the crystal results in Table 3.4. Thus the changes in Table 3.6 could be a feature of the more rigorous methods used, but the results do seem unreasonably large, with those for phenanthrene particularly suspect given that the principal components of polarizability must be non-negative in the ground state.

Examination of the numerical data entering the calculations shows that the

Table 3.6 Effective molecular polarizability components in crystals [53] referred to molecular *LMN* axes and to principal axes

Molecule	$\alpha/10^{-40}$ F m^2	
	Molecular axes	Principal axes
Naphthalene	$\begin{pmatrix} 42.2 & -5.2 & 7.1 \\ & 19.1 & -2.4 \\ & & 11.8 \end{pmatrix}$	$\begin{pmatrix} 45.0 & & \\ & 18.1 & \\ & & 10.1 \end{pmatrix}$
Anthracene	$\begin{pmatrix} 70.4 & -7.5 & 13.6 \\ & 24.7 & -3.0 \\ & & 14.6 \end{pmatrix}$	$\begin{pmatrix} 75.4 & & \\ & 22.9 & \\ & & 11.4 \end{pmatrix}$
Phenanthrene	$\begin{pmatrix} 96.8 & 2.9 & -9.5 \\ & 19.3 & 5.1 \\ & & 4.0 \end{pmatrix}$	$\begin{pmatrix} 97.8 & & \\ & 20.8 & \\ & & 1.4 \end{pmatrix}$
Biphenyl	$\begin{pmatrix} 63.6 & 1.6 & 6.2 \\ & 19.3 & 0.0 \\ & & 8.6 \end{pmatrix}$	$\begin{pmatrix} 64.7 & & \\ & 19.3 & \\ & & 7.1 \end{pmatrix}$

Table 3.7 Mean molecular polarizabilities $\alpha = \frac{1}{3}\,\mathrm{Tr}\,\boldsymbol{\alpha}$ and polarizability anisotropies $\Delta\alpha = \frac{1}{2}(\alpha_{LL} + \alpha_{MM}) - \alpha_{NN}$ in the crystal and in the free state

	$\alpha/10^{-40}$ F m^2			$\Delta\alpha/10^{-40}$ F m^2		
	Free[a]	Crystal[a]	Crystal[b]	Free[a]	Crystal[a]	Crystal[b]
Naphthalene	18.1	18.9	24.4	7.8	10.8	21.4
Anthracene	25.1	25.9	36.6	11.3	11.1	37.8
Phenanthrene	25.1	25.7	40.0	11.3	31.0	57.9
Biphenyl	—	22.9	30.4	—	12.5	34.9

[a] Table 3.4.
[b] Table 3.6.

anisotropy of $\boldsymbol{a}$ is directly related to that of the $\boldsymbol{L}_{kk'}$. Indeed, from equation (3.5.20) and the definition of the $\boldsymbol{M}_{kk'}$ it can be seen that when $\boldsymbol{L}_{kk'}$ is large, $\boldsymbol{a}_k$ will tend to be small, and conversely. If the effective polarizability is too anisotropic, then this reflects Lorentz-factor tensors which are too anistropic. This feature can be traced to the approximation implicit in equation (3.5.3) of treating molecules as points for the purpose of calculating dipole fields. For elongated molecules, some regions of adjacent molecules approach much more closely than the centres of the molecules, and since dipole fields vary as $1/r^3$ the effective anisotropy of the dipole field is less than that of a lattice of point dipoles at the molecular centres. It is therefore necessary to go beyond the point-dipole approximation.

A practical means of achieving the necessary extension was presented by

Luty [55]. He treated molecules composed of crystallographically or chemically equivalent submolecules: iodine (equivalent atoms), naphthalene (equivalent rings) and hexachlorobenzene (equivalent C—Cl moieties). One can calculate Lorentz-factor tensors $\boldsymbol{L}(kj, k'j')$ between pairs of submolecules j and j' on sublattices k and k', omitting contributions between submolecules in the same molecule because a molecule does not polarize itself, and one then obtains averaged Lorentz-factor tensors given by

$$\boldsymbol{L}_{kk'} = s^{-2} \sum_{jj'} \boldsymbol{L}(kj, k'j') \tag{3.5.22}$$

where s is the number of submolecules per molecule. These are used instead of the point-dipole Lorentz-factor tensors.

Luty also introduced implicitly a way of treating the problem of arbitrariness already noted, which is not removed by the submolecule treatment. From equation (3.5.19) one can derive an equation for $\boldsymbol{a}_k^{-1}$ by writing $\boldsymbol{F}_k = \boldsymbol{d}_k \cdot \boldsymbol{E}$, eliminating $\boldsymbol{E}$, and multiplying on the right by $(\boldsymbol{a}_k \cdot \boldsymbol{d}_k)^{-1}$, to obtain [54]

$$\boldsymbol{a}_k^{-1} = \boldsymbol{M}_{kk} + \sum_{k'(\neq k)} \boldsymbol{M}_{kk'} \cdot \boldsymbol{p}_{k'k} \tag{3.5.23}$$

Here

$$\boldsymbol{p}_{k'k} = (\boldsymbol{a}_{k'} \cdot \boldsymbol{d}_{k'}) \cdot (\boldsymbol{a}_k \cdot \boldsymbol{d}_k)^{-1} \tag{3.5.24}$$

is the ratio between the contribution of sublattices k' and k to $\boldsymbol{\chi}$, whence it follows that the $\boldsymbol{p}_{k'k}$ must satisfy

$$\boldsymbol{\chi} = \left(\boldsymbol{1} + \sum_{k'(\neq k)} \boldsymbol{p}_{k'k}\right) \cdot \boldsymbol{a}_k \cdot \boldsymbol{d}_k. \tag{3.5.25}$$

If the sublattices are crystallographically or chemically equivalent, it is plausible to assume that they each make the same contribution to $\boldsymbol{\chi}$, in which case $\boldsymbol{p}_{k'k} = \boldsymbol{1}$ for all k, k' and $\boldsymbol{a}_k \cdot \boldsymbol{d}_k = \boldsymbol{\chi}/Z$. Furthermore, the inverse polarizability then follows from equation (3.5.23) as

$$\boldsymbol{a}_k^{-1} = \sum_{k'} \boldsymbol{M}_{kk'} \tag{3.5.26}$$

where now the sum over k' is unrestricted.

Alternatively, one can derive equations similar to (3.5.23)–(3.5.26) before averaging over submolecules, to obtain submolecule effective polarizabilities given by

$$\boldsymbol{a}_{kj}^{-1} = \sum_{k'j'} \boldsymbol{M}(kj, k'j') \tag{3.5.27}$$

where $\boldsymbol{M}(kj, k'j') = \boldsymbol{\chi}^{-1} + \boldsymbol{L}(kj, k'j')$. A molecular polarizability is then obtained by summing the submolecule polarizabilities over all submolecules. If all submolecules are crystallographically equivalent, the result coincides with $\boldsymbol{M}_k$ obtained from (3.5.26), but in general we have

$$\boldsymbol{a}_k^{-1} = s^{-2} \sum_j \boldsymbol{a}_{kj}^{-1} \tag{3.5.28}$$

Since bond or atom additivity schemes for polarizability work well, it is possible to argue that the molecular polarizability is better calculated from the submolecule polarizabilities (3.5.27) rather than from (3.5.26). On the other hand, schemes for adding *inverse* bond or atom polarizabilities in some way like (3.5.28) have not been tried and could be equally good. Moreover, since both routes to the effective polarizability rely on the approximation that all sublattices or submolecules contribute equally to $\boldsymbol{\chi}$, the simpler method of averaging $\boldsymbol{L}$ over submolecules and retaining the point-molecule algebra arguably represents a reasonable compromise between the demands of ease and rigour.

Polarizabilities obtained as the sum of submolecule polarizabilities are given in Table 3.8 together with polarizabilities obtained by the iteration method using point molecules and obtained by the usual composite of methods for the isolated molecule. For iodine the submolecule method reduces the anisotropy for the iteration method to a value closer to that for the isolated molecule. For hexachlorobenzene the submolecule method gives a polarizability more anisotropic than for the isolated molecule, but it removes the unphysical negative principal value given by the iteration method. For naphthalene the submolecule method reduces the anisotropy compared with the iteration method to yield a polarizability very close to that for the isolated molecule. Similarly, calculations for biphenyl in the point-dipole treatment yield one component of polarizability three orders of magnitude larger than for the isolated molecule, whereas the submolecule treatment yields results closely similar to those for the isolated molecule [57].

It therefore appears that the submolecule treatment gives polarizabilities sufficiently close to those for the isolated molecule to allow one confidence in their general reliability. In fact, deducing polarizabilities for isolated molecules demands considerable time and effort which is seldom provided except for more symmetrical molecules. In the case of molecules without any special symmetry, the submolecule treatment may be the most direct route to any form of polarizability (apart from the average), provided reasonable sized crystals can be grown for the determination of the refractive indices. A selection of such polarizabilities is given in Section 3.6.

The submolecule treatment also gives reasonable local fields. Since the point-molecule treatment exaggerates the anisotropy of the polarizability but is constrained to give the observed susceptibility, which is a product of the local field and the polarizability by (3.5.14), this treatment tends to underestimate the local field anisotropy or to generate anisotropy in the wrong direction. The same is true in a less extreme form for the anisotropic Lorentz local field. This in effect ignores any anisotropy in the Lorentz-factor tensors so that all anisotropy arises from the polarizabilities; cf. equations (3.4.16)

Table 3.8 Polarizabilities $\boldsymbol{\alpha}/10^{-40}\ \mathrm{F\,m^2}$ in the molecular axes obtained using the point molecule iteration method and the submolecule method, with isolated molecular polarizabilities for comparison [55]

Crystal	Iteration	Submolecules	Isolated
Iodine (*Cmca*)	$\begin{pmatrix} 7.6 & 0 & 0 \\ & 14.6 & -7.9 \\ & & 30.4 \end{pmatrix}$	$\begin{pmatrix} 8.7 & 0 & 0 \\ & 17.7 & 5.3 \\ & & 16.0 \end{pmatrix}$	$\begin{pmatrix} 8.0 & 0 & 0 \\ & 8.0 & 0 \\ & & 17.7 \end{pmatrix}$
Hexachlorobenzene ($P2_1/c$)	$\begin{pmatrix} 17.2 & 19.3 & -7.4 \\ & 16.0 & -41.5 \\ & & 25.6 \end{pmatrix}$	$\begin{pmatrix} 14.1 & -1.7 & -6.7 \\ & 42.1 & 5.5 \\ & & 37.3 \end{pmatrix}$	$\begin{pmatrix} 17.1 & 0 & 0 \\ & 28.2 & 0 \\ & & 28.2 \end{pmatrix}$
Naphthalene ($P2_1/a$)	$\begin{pmatrix} 41.0 & 8.7 & 20.4 \\ & 21.1 & 7.7 \\ & & 17.6 \end{pmatrix}$	$\begin{pmatrix} 24.3 & 3.9 & -0.2 \\ & 19.0 & 3.8 \\ & & 15.4 \end{pmatrix}$	$\begin{pmatrix} 23.9 & 0 & 0 \\ & 19.6 & 0 \\ & & 11.5 \end{pmatrix}$

and (3.4.17). Calculations for *p*-terphenyl show this effect clearly [58]: the anisotropies of the anisotropic Lorentz local field and of the submolecule local field are opposite in sign, with the submolecule local field leading to a physically preferable interpretation of electronic Stark effect measurements.

Hitherto, the local electric fields treated here have been those produced by a uniform macroscopic field or applied field. Rigorous molecular theories can also be developed to describe dielectric and optical response to non-uniform fields such as arise in several applications. Suppose molecule k in unit cell l is subjected to an applied field $\boldsymbol{E}^0_{lk}$. Then the local fields are given by

$$\boldsymbol{F}_{lk} = \boldsymbol{F}^0_{lk} + \sum_{l'k'} \boldsymbol{T}_{lk,l'k'} \cdot \boldsymbol{a}_{k'} \cdot \boldsymbol{F}_{l'k'} \tag{3.5.29}$$

where $\boldsymbol{T}_{lk,l'k'}$ is the dipole tensor $(v/4\pi)\nabla\nabla(1/r)$ in the limit $\boldsymbol{r} \to \boldsymbol{r}_{lk} - \boldsymbol{r}_{l'k'}$. Fourier transformation, using the fact that $\boldsymbol{T}$ depends only on the difference $l - l'$ because of translational symmetry, yields the set of equations

$$\boldsymbol{f}_k(\boldsymbol{y}) = \boldsymbol{e}^0_k(\boldsymbol{y}) + \sum_{k'} \boldsymbol{t}_{kk'}(\boldsymbol{y}) \cdot \boldsymbol{a}_{k'} \cdot \boldsymbol{f}_{k'}(\boldsymbol{y}) \tag{3.5.30}$$

where lower-case letters are Fourier transforms and $\boldsymbol{y}$ is the wavevector. For each $\boldsymbol{y}$ there are now Z equations which can be solved to obtain [59]

$$\boldsymbol{f}_k(\boldsymbol{y}) = \sum_{k'} \boldsymbol{\epsilon}^{-1}_{kk'}(\boldsymbol{y}) \cdot \boldsymbol{e}^0_{k'}(\boldsymbol{y}) \tag{3.5.31}$$

where $\boldsymbol{\epsilon}^{-1}_{kk'}(\boldsymbol{y})$ is the inverse dielectric tensor such that

$$\boldsymbol{\epsilon}^{-1}_{kk'}(\boldsymbol{y}) = [\boldsymbol{1} - \boldsymbol{t}(\boldsymbol{y}) \cdot \boldsymbol{A}]^{-1}_{kk'}; \tag{3.5.32}$$

here $\boldsymbol{t}$ is the $3Z \times 3Z$ matrix having the $\boldsymbol{t}_{kk'}$ as 3×3 submatrices and $\boldsymbol{A}$ is again the $3Z \times 3Z$ matrix having $\boldsymbol{a}_k \delta_{kk'}$ as 3×3 submatrices.

As can be seen, the inverse dielectric function contains very general information about the dielectric response of the crystal, giving the local fields in terms of arbitrary applied fields. In the general dielectric theory of solids, inverting the dielectric function is a difficult task most often achieved only in a formal sense. In molecular crystals, however, the separate molecular polarizabilities $\boldsymbol{a}_k$ allow a direct algebraic inversion. Note also that the inverse dielectric tensor is non-local, with the field on one sublattice depending on the applied fields on other sublattices as well.

Applications of these results depend on the form of the applied field. For a uniform applied field, only the limit $\boldsymbol{y} \to 0$ is required. In this case the lattice dipole sum is separated into

$$\boldsymbol{t}_{kk'}(\boldsymbol{y}) = \boldsymbol{L}_{kk'}(\boldsymbol{y}) - \boldsymbol{y}\boldsymbol{y}/|\boldsymbol{y}|^2 \tag{3.5.33}$$

where $\boldsymbol{L}_{kk'}(\boldsymbol{y})$ tends to the Lorentz-factor tensor as $\boldsymbol{y} \to 0$. The last term in (3.5.33) is irregular as $\boldsymbol{y} \to 0$, its value depending on the way in which $\boldsymbol{y}$ approaches zero (e.g. along one axis or uniformly in all directions). This irregularity reflects the shape dependence of dipole polarization, but can be treated by noting that the irregular part substituted in (3.5.30) yields the field due to the macroscopic polarization, which can be combined with the applied field $\boldsymbol{e}_k^0(\boldsymbol{y})$ to give the macroscopic field $\boldsymbol{e}(\boldsymbol{y})$. This field is uniform only in an ellipsoidal sample, but this problem is now transferred to the macroscopic field, which is a matter of the experimental conditions, leaving the microscopic contribution, which is the fact of major interest, as characteristic of the crystal structure and not of the sample shape. If the local fields are expressed in terms of the macroscopic fields, then $\boldsymbol{e}$ replaces $\boldsymbol{e}^0$ and $\boldsymbol{L}$ replaces $\boldsymbol{t}$, with the result

$$f_k(\boldsymbol{y}) = \sum_{k'} \boldsymbol{D}_{kk'}(\boldsymbol{y}) \cdot \boldsymbol{e}_{k'}(\boldsymbol{y}) \tag{3.5.34}$$

which is a slight generalization of (3.5.11), in which the local field tensor $\boldsymbol{D}$ is expressed in terms of $\boldsymbol{L}(\boldsymbol{y})$ instead of the $\boldsymbol{y}=0$ limit $\boldsymbol{L}$.

If the applied fields are due to displacements of molecules from their equilibrium positions during a lattice vibration, these results can be used to derive expressions for the intensities of lattice vibrational spectra. For Raman and infrared spectra, the long-wavelength limit $\boldsymbol{y} \to 0$ is appropriate, and in each case the key quantity is the dipole induced by the molecular displacements, which is governed by the susceptibility contributions $\boldsymbol{\chi}_{kk'}$ already referred to. For example, the infrared absorption intensity for a given mode is a sum of the $\boldsymbol{\chi}_{kk'}$ weighted by the eigenvectors of the mode describing the displacements of each sublattice and by quantities describing the field produced at each sublattice by the displacements [60]. Similar considerations govern the intensity of Raman scattering [61] and of Brillouin scattering [62], where in both cases it is necessary to take proper account of crystal optics to relate the light incident on the sample to that emitted from it [63].

Non-uniform applied fields are produced by an impurity molecule. This could be a molecule carrying an excess charge (a molecular ion) or a molecule with a different dipole moment from the host crystal molecules (which could be a host molecule in an excited electronic state) or a molecule with any permanent multipole moment different from the host molecules. In such cases it is often the energy which is of interest, and the part of the energy common to all such cases is the polarization energy P. This gives the energy change produced as the applied field due to the impurity-induced dipole moments through the crystal, and has the general form [64, 65]

$$P = -\tfrac{1}{2} \sum_{lk} \boldsymbol{E}_{lk}^0 \cdot \boldsymbol{p}_{lk}. \tag{3.5.35}$$

Here the induced dipoles are obtained from the polarizabilities and the local fields, so that the key to the problem is the relation between the local fields and the applied fields which is provided by (3.5.31). In practice, the sum over l in (3.5.35) is conveniently transformed to a sum of the Fourier transformed fields and dipoles over the wavevector $\boldsymbol{y}$, and then (3.5.31) can be used directly [66]. This treatment also allows the long-range behaviour $\boldsymbol{y} \to 0$ to be treated separately by using (3.5.33) in (3.5.32), thereby yielding the macroscopic dielectric behaviour from a microscopic treatment.

These approaches have been applied to several problems. One of the earliest was the electronic Stark effect, a first-order splitting produced by applying an electric field to a molecular crystal containing guest molecules in different sites which lose their degeneracy in the field [65, 67, 68]. This work also solves the problem of the change in the crystal dielectric response due to the replacement of a host molecule with a guest molecule of different polarizability. The field due to a dipole has also been treated more generally [69]. The energy due to an excess charge has been treated in progressively more rigorous ways [66, 70–72], including the effect of imperfections with altered polarizabilities such as vacancies and excitons [73–75]. Considerable interest attaches to charge-transfer excitons in molecular crystals, comprising an electron and a hole on different molecules. Charge-transfer excitons are believed to play an essential role in photogeneration of charge carriers, but in aromatic hydrocarbons direct spectroscopic detection of charge-transfer states proved elusive until electroabsorption studies were performed [76]. The electrostatic energy of charge-transfer excitons can be calculated by a direct extension of polarization energy calculations for a single carrier, augmented by a Coulomb energy term [77–79]. These calculations allow deviations from a Coulomb $1/r$ behaviour to be detected at small distances between electron and hole, they yield the apparent dielectric constant describing the screened Coulomb interaction at long distances in an arbitrary direction, and they provide the basis for a quantitative interpretation of the electroabsorption spectra [78, 79]

3.6 TABLE OF CRYSTAL AND MOLECULAR PROPERTIES

This table is arranged in essentially the same way as Section 2.5. For ease of reference, structural data are repeated for crystals common to both tables. There are also some differences of detail where different authors have presented results based on different recalculated direction cosines.

Unit-cell dimensions are quoted as $a/10^{-10}$ m, etc. Wavelengths for optical susceptibilities are quoted as λ/nm. Polarizabilities are quoted in terms of polarizability volumes $(\alpha/4\pi\varepsilon_0)/10^{-30}\ m^3$, corresponding to $\alpha_{cgs}/10^{-24}\ cm^3$. Polarizability components not determined uniquely by symmetry are obtained from the $\rho = 0$ solution.

3.6.1 Benzene, C_6H_6

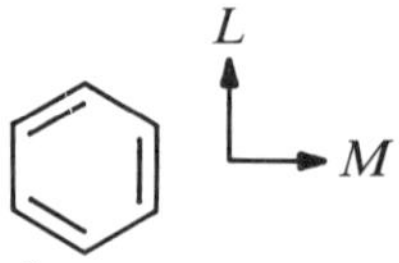

(1) Crystal structure [77]
Space group *Pbca*, with $a = 7.460$, $b = 9.666$, $c = 7.033$ Å, and $Z = 4$. A

single submolecule is located at the centre of the ring, for comparison with other aromatic hydrocarbons treated as one submolecule for each ring.

Direction cosines for the molecular axes relative to the crystal axes [57]:

	a	b	c
L	−0.276	0.961	−0.029
M	−0.649	−0.163	0.743
N	0.709	0.224	0.668

(2) Crystal susceptibilities [78]

χ_{aa}	χ_{bb}	χ_{cc}	λ
1.3839	1.7093	1.4025	546

(3) Lorentz-factor tensors [57]

kk'	L_{aa}	L_{bb}	L_{cc}
11	0.421	0.047	0.532
12	−0.224	0.936	0.288
13	0.970	−0.759	0.789
14	0.323	0.844	−0.167

(4) Polarizability volumes

	α_{LL}	α_{LM}	α_{LN}	α_{MM}	α_{MN}	α_{NN}
[57]	11.62	−0.42	0.56	9.38	−0.00	9.42
free	12.5	0	0	12.5	0	8.2

3.6.2 Naphthalene, $C_{10}H_8$

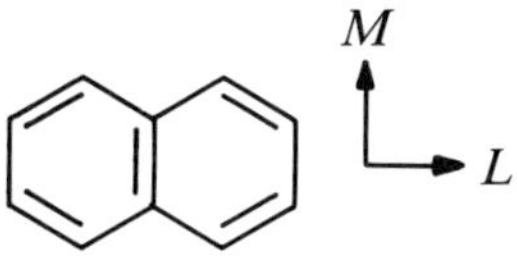

(1) Crystal structure [79]

Space group $P2_1/a$, with $a = 8.235$, $b = 6.003$, $c = 8.658$ Å, $\beta = 122.92°$, and $Z = 2$. A submolecule is located at the centre of each ring.

Direction cosines for the molecular axes relative to the crystal axes [78]:

	a	b	c^*
L	−0.4379	−0.2103	0.8741
M	−0.3207	−0.8718	−0.3704
N	0.8399	−0.4425	0.3143

(2) Crystal susceptibilities [18]

χ_{aa}	χ_{ac^*}	χ_{bb}	$\chi_{c^*c^*}$	λ
1.555	−0.531	1.965	2.553	546

(3) Lorentz-factor tensors [57]

kk'	L_{aa}	L_{ab}	L_{ac^*}	L_{bb}	L_{bc^*}	$L_{c^*c^*}$
11	0.230	−0.017	−0.001	0.524	0.034	0.245
12	0.693	0	0.144	0.306	0	0.000

(4) Polarizability volumes

	α_{LL}	α_{LM}	α_{LN}	α_{MM}	α_{MN}	α_{NN}
[57]	18.9	−2.2	0.9	10.1	0.8	8.1
free	21.8	0	0	19.6	0	12.9

3.6.3 Anthracene, $C_{14}H_{10}$

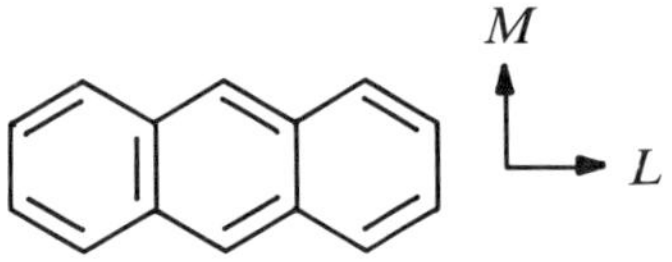

(1) Crystal structure [80]
Space group $P2_1/a$, with $a = 8.562$, $b = 6.038$, $c = 11.184$ Å, $\beta = 124.70°$, and $Z = 2$. A submolecule is located at the centre of each ring.

Direction cosines for the molecular axes relative to the crystal axes [81]:

	a	b	c^*
L	−0.4941	−0.1274	0.8600
M	−0.3175	−0.8944	−0.3149
N	0.8094	−0.4287	0.4015

(2) Crystal susceptibilities [18]

χ_{aa}	χ_{ac^*}	χ_{bb}	$\chi_{c^*c^*}$	λ
1.717	−0.576	2.190	2.542	540

(3) Lorentz-factor tensors [57]

kk'	L_{aa}	L_{ab}	L_{ac^*}	L_{bb}	L_{bc^*}	$L_{c^*c^*}$
11	0.234	−0.019	0.031	0.566	0.033	0.200
12	0.654	0	0.224	0.306	0	0.040

(4) Polarizability volumes

	α_{LL}	α_{LM}	α_{LN}	α_{MM}	α_{MN}	α_{NN}
[57]	30.0	−2.2	1.3	14.2	1.2	11.8
free	31.1	0	0	26.7	0	17.6

3.6.4 Phenanthrene, $C_{14}H_{10}$

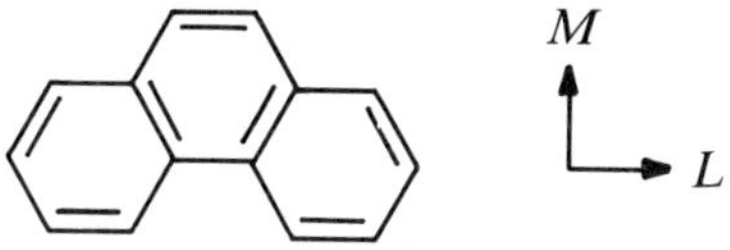

(1) Crystal structure [80]
Space group $P2_1/a$, with $a = 8.472$, $b = 6.166$, $c = 9.467$ Å, $\beta = 98.01°$, and $Z = 2$. A submolecule is located at the centre of each ring.
Direction cosines for the molecular axes relative to the crystal axes [82]:

	a	b	c^*
L	0.2387	0.0594	0.9693
M	0.4535	0.8757	−0.1659
N	−0.8587	0.4792	0.1821

(2) Crystal susceptibilities [82]

χ_{aa}	χ_{ac^*}	χ_{bb}	$\chi_{c^*c^*}$	λ
1.443	0.242	1.972	2.639	540

(3) Lorentz-factor tensors [57]

kk'	L_{aa}	L_{ab}	L_{ac^*}	L_{bb}	L_{bc^*}	$L_{c^*c^*}$
11	0.146	0.029	−0.056	0.619	0.025	0.235
12	0.862	0	−0.080	0.219	0	−0.081

(4) Polarizability volumes

	α_{LL}	α_{LM}	α_{LN}	α_{MM}	α_{MN}	α_{NN}
[57]	44.1	−2.5	1.5	20.3	1.9	16.9
free	30.0	0	0	27.8	0	17.6

3.6.5 Pyrene, $C_{16}H_{10}$

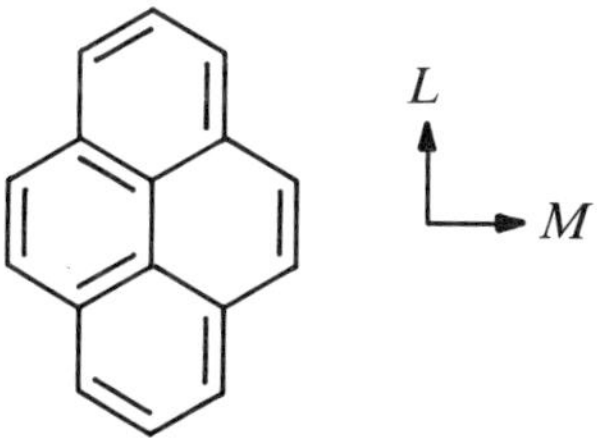

(1) Crystal structure [83]
Space group $P2_1/a$, with $a = 13.469$, $b = 9.256$, $c = 8.470$ Å, $\beta = 100.47°$, and $Z = 4$. Submolecules are located at the centres of the rings.

Direction cosines for the molecular axes relative to the crystal axes [84]:

	a	b	c^*
L	0.4834	0.2130	0.8487
M	0.6130	0.6101	−0.5017
N	−0.6248	0.7630	0.1648

(2) Crystal susceptibilities [84]

$\chi_{\alpha\alpha}$	χ_{ac^*}	χ_{bb}	$\chi_{c^*c^*}$	λ
1.83	−0.35	2.07	2.66	static

(3) Lorentz-factor tensors [85]

kk'	L_{aa}	L_{ab}	L_{ac^*}	L_{bb}	L_{bc^*}	$L_{c^*c^*}$
11	−0.019	−0.017	−0.220	0.371	−0.007	0.649
12	0.596	−0.965	0.091	0.720	−0.011	−0.316
13	0.964	0	0.076	0.012	0	0.025
14	0.286	0	−0.079	0.715	0	−0.001

(4) Polarizability volumes

	α_{LL}	α_{LM}	α_{LN}	α_{MM}	α_{MN}	α_{NN}
[85]	37.2	−7.6	5.4	33.9	−1.2	17.3
free	35.1	0	0	35.1	0	14.5

3.6.6 Biphenyl, $C_{12}H_{10}$

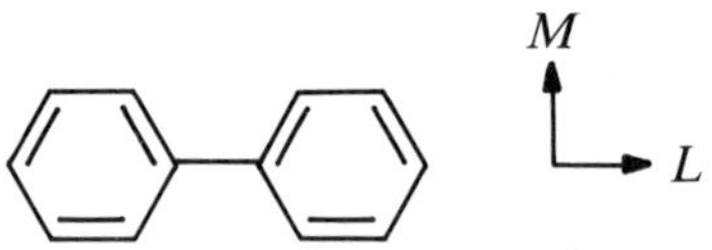

(1) Crystal structure [39]
Space group $P2_1/a$, with $a = 8.63$, $b = 5.63$, $c = 9.15$ Å, $\beta = 95.1°$, and $Z = 2$. Submolecules are located at the centre of each ring.

Direction cosines for the molecular axes relative to the crystal axes [57]:

	a	b	c^*
L	0.294	−0.021	0.955
M	0.534	−0.826	−0.183
N	−0.793	−0.564	0.232

(2) Crystal susceptibilities [82]

χ_{aa}	χ_{ac^*}	χ_{bb}	$\chi_{c^*c^*}$	λ
1.532	0.345	1.749	2.688	546

(3) Lorentz-factor tensors [57]

kk'	L_{aa}	L_{ab}	L_{ac^*}	L_{bb}	L_{bc^*}	$L_{c^*c^*}$
11	0.152	0.001	−0.082	0.592	0.007	0.256
12	0.768	0	−0.040	0.230	0	0.002

(4) Polarizability volumes

	α_{LL}	α_{LM}	α_{LN}	α_{MM}	α_{MN}	α_{NN}
[85]	36.0	−0.1	−0.3	17.1	1.2	16.1
free	25.4	0	0	20.8	0	14.1

3.6.7 *p*-Terphenyl, $C_{18}H_{14}$

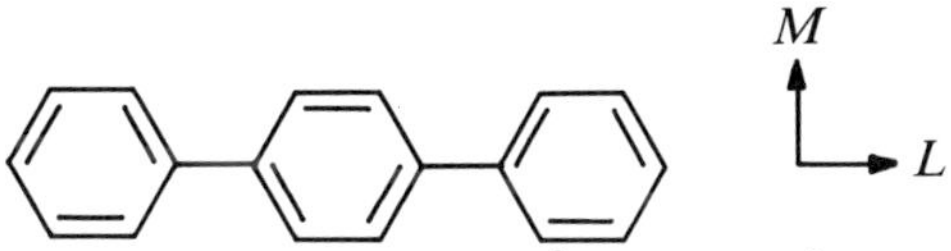

(1) Crystal structure [86]
Space group $P2_1/a$, with $a = 8.08$, $b = 5.60$, $c = 13.59$ Å, $\beta = 91.9°$, and $Z = 2$. Submolecules are located at the centre of each ring.
Direction cosines for the molecular axes relative to the crystal axes [87]:

	a	b	c^*
L	0.2933	0.0071	0.9597
M	0.5158	0.8414	−0.1643
N	−0.8050	0.5404	0.2470

(2) Crystal susceptibilities [82]

χ_{aa}	χ_{ac^*}	χ_{bb}	$\chi_{c^*c^*}$	λ
1.622	−0.397	1.846	2.903	546

(3) Lorentz-factor tensors [57]

kk'	L_{aa}	L_{ab}	L_{ac^*}	L_{bb}	L_{bc^*}	$L_{c^*c^*}$
11	0.181	−0.000	0.073	0.635	0.001	0.184
12	0.759	0	0.092	0.227	0	0.014

(4) Polarizability volumes [57]

α_{LL}	α_{LM}	α_{LN}	α_{MM}	α_{MN}	α_{NN}
59.4	−1.4	−1.9	24.1	−1.7	22.5

3.6.8 *p*-Nitroaniline, $C_6H_6N_2O_2$

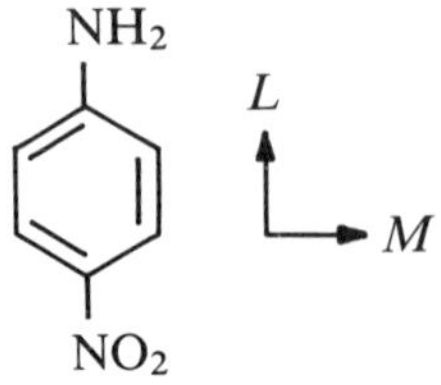

(1) Crystal structure [45]
Space group $P2_1/n$, with $a = 12.336$, $b = 6.07$, $c = 8.592$ Å, $\beta = 91.45°$, and $Z = 4$. Submolecules are located at the centre of the ring and at each nitrogen.
Direction cosines for the molecular axes relative to the crystal axes [88]:

	a	b	c^*
L	−0.7594	0.4428	0.4766
M	0.0981	0.8022	−0.5889
N	0.6431	0.4005	0.6527

(2) Crystal susceptibilities [27]

χ_{aa}	χ_{ac^*}	χ_{bb}	$\chi_{c^*c^*}$	λ
1.704	−0.432	2.084	1.819	590

(3) Lorentz-factor tensors [88]

kk'	L_{aa}	L_{ab}	L_{ac^*}	L_{bb}	L_{bc^*}	$L_{c^*c^*}$
11	−0.006	0.164	0.004	0.773	−0.107	0.233
12	0.190	0	0.487	0.072	0	0.739
13	0.586	0.107	0.522	−0.078	0.159	0.492
14	0.528	0	−0.315	0.338	0	0.134

(4) Polarizability volumes [87]

α_{LL}	α_{LM}	α_{LN}	α_{MM}	α_{MN}	α_{NN}
19.9	−0.9	1.2	16.3	1.7	10.5

3.6.9 *m*-Nitroaniline, $C_6H_6N_2O_2$

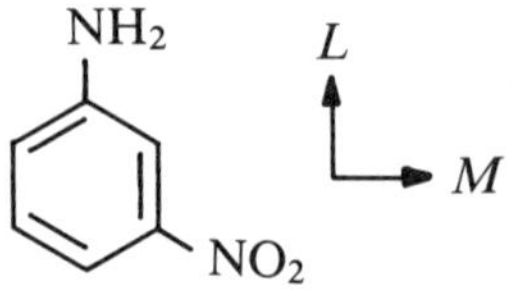

(1) Crystal structure [89]
Space group $Pbc2_1$, with $a = 6.501$, $b = 19.330$, $c = 5.082$ Å, and $Z = 4$. Submolecules are located at the centre of the ring and at each nitrogen.

Direction cosines for the molecular axes relative to the crystal axes [90]:

	a	b	c
L	−0.5979	−0.7897	−0.1400
M	0.6021	−0.3267	−0.7282
N	0.5291	−0.5193	0.6709

(2) Crystal susceptibilities [91]

χ_{aa}	χ_{bb}	χ_{cc}	λ
2.0276	1.9241	1.7225	532
2.2761	2.2041	1.9584	1064

(3) Lorentz-factor tensors [90]

kk'	L_{aa}	L_{ab}	L_{ac}	L_{bb}	L_{bc}	L_{cc}
11	1.110	−0.343	−0.516	−1.692	0.075	1.582
12	−0.028	0	−0.001	0.749	0	0.280
13	0.023	−0.009	0	0.964	0	0.013
14	−0.001	0	0	1.001	−0.000	−0.000

(4) Polarizability volumes [90]

α_{LL}	α_{LM}	α_{LN}	α_{MM}	α_{MN}	α_{NN}	λ
18.8	0.4	0.1	11.9	1.3	15.3	532
20.9	0.4	−0.7	15.9	1.7	13.1	1064

3.6.10 Tetracyanoquinodimethane (TCNQ), $C_{12}H_4N_4$

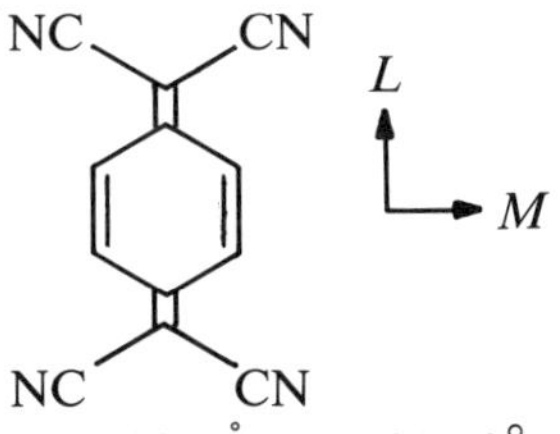

(1) Crystal structure [92]
Space group $C2/c$, with $a = 8.906$, $b = 7.060$, $c = 16.395$ Å, $\beta = 98.53°$, and $Z = 4$. Submolecules are located at the centre of the ring and at each cyano carbon.

Direction cosines for the molecular axes relative to the crystal axes [93]:

	a	b	c^*
L	0.6595	0.2708	0.7012
M	0.7500	−0.3001	−0.5895
N	0.0508	0.9146	−0.4011

(2) Crystal susceptibilities [94]

χ_{aa}	χ_{ac^*}	χ_{bb}	$\chi_{c^*c^*}$	λ
3.882	0	1.334	2.033	500

(3) Lorentz-factor tensors [93]

kk'	L_{aa}	L_{ab}	L_{ac^*}	L_{bb}	L_{bc^*}	$L_{c^*c^*}$
11	0.436	−0.076	−0.211	0.578	−0.043	−0.013
12	0.367	0	0.121	−0.165	0	0.798
13	0.381	0.015	−0.066	0.936	−0.410	−0.317
14	−0.209	0	−0.054	0.513	0	0.696

(4) Polarizability volumes [93]

α_{LL}	α_{LM}	α_{LN}	α_{MM}	α_{MN}	α_{NN}
58.9	−8.2	9.7	42.1	7.7	20.1

3.6.11 Pyromellitic dianhydride (PMDA), $C_{10}H_2O_6$

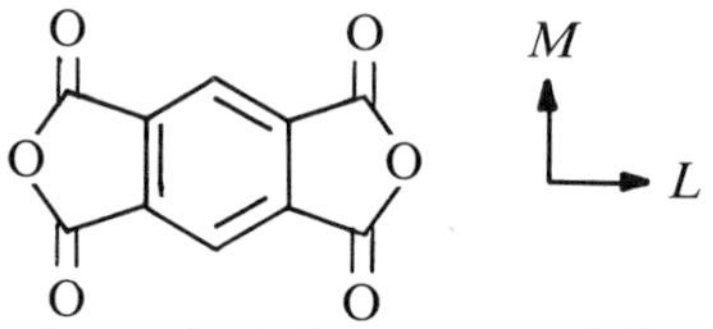

(1) Crystal structure [95]
Space group $P4_2/n$, with $a = b = 10.792$, $c = 7.413$ Å, and $Z = 4$. Submolecules are located at the centre of the aromatic ring and at each carbonyl carbon atom.

Direction cosines for the molecular axes relative to the crystal axes [93]:

	a	b	c
L	0.598	0.734	0.734
M	−0.322	0.598	−0.322
N	0.734	0.734	0.598

(2) Crystal susceptibilities [96]

χ_{aa}	χ_{bb}	χ_{cc}	λ
1.595	1.595	1.449	625

(3) Lorentz-factor tensors [93]

kk'	L_{aa}	L_{ab}	L_{ac}	L_{bb}	L_{bc}	L_{cc}
11	0.018	−0.040	0.082	0.345	−0.187	0.637
12	1.029	−0.078	0	0.094	0	−0.123
13	−0.237	0.064	0.210	0.883	0.196	0.354
14	0.883	−0.064	0.196	−0.237	−0.210	0.354

(4) Polarizability volumes [93]

α_{LL}	α_{LM}	α_{LN}	α_{MM}	α_{MN}	α_{NN}
16.6	0.4	−2.0	19.2	−0.9	17.6

3.6.12 Carbazole, $C_{12}H_9N$

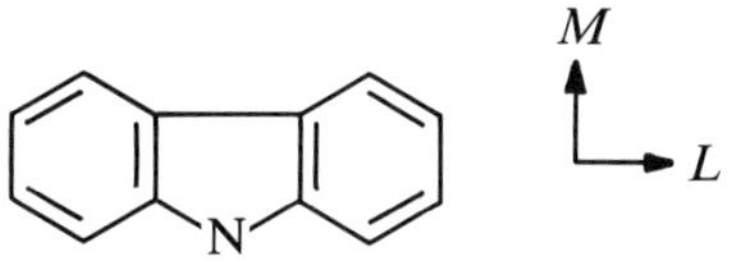

(1) Crystal structure [97]
Space group *Pnma* with $a = 7.77$, $b = 19.18$, $c = 5.72$ Å, and $Z = 4$. Submolecules are located at the C and N atoms.
The molecular L axis lies parallel to the crystal b axis, and the molecular N axis makes an angle $\theta = 61.2°$ with the crystal c axis [98].

(2) Crystal susceptibilities [98]

χ_{aa}	χ_{bb}	χ_{cc}	λ
1.4336	3.2312	1.9791	546

(3) Lorentz-factor tensors [99]

kk'	L_{aa}	$L_{ac} = L_{ca}$	L_{bb}	L_{cc}
11	0.290	−0.210	−0.525	1.235
12	0.068	−0.006	0.950	−0.018
13	−0.047	0	1.014	0.034
14	1.716	0	−0.970	0.255

(4) Polarizability volumes

		α_{LL}	α_{MM}	α_{MN}	α_{NN}
	[99]	39.8	18.8	−1.7	14.6
bond contrib.	[98]	26.4	21.9	0	14.8

3.6.13 Urea, CH_4N_2O

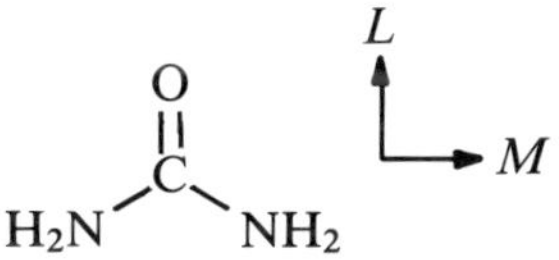

(1) Crystal structure [100]
Space group $P\bar{4}2_1m$, with $a = b = 5.661$, $c = 4.712$ Å, and $Z = 2$. The molecules lie with their L axes antiparallel along the c axis and with their planes perpendicular to one another at angles of 45° to the a and b axes.

(2) Crystal susceptibilities [101]

χ_{aa}	χ_{cc}	λ
1.2091	1.5341	597

(3) Lorentz-factor tensors [102]

kk'	L_{aa}	L_{ab}	L_{bb}	L_{cc}
11	0.190	−0.230	0.190	0.620
12	0.445	0	0.445	0.110

(4) Polarizability volumes [102]

α_{LL}	α_{LM}	α_{LN}	α_{MM}	α_{MN}	α_{NN}
5.9	0	0	5.2	0	5.3

3.6.14 Iodoform, CHI_3

(1) Crystal structure
The structure of iodoform is hexagonal and has been assigned to the space group R3m with $a = 6.818$, $c = 7.524$ Å, and $Z = 2$ [103], corresponding to two antiparallel orientations of the iodoform molecules along the hexagonal axis. Later work indicates that the structure is disordered [104], but the details have not been elucidated. The ordered structure will therefore be used here: disordering should make only a minor difference, and iodoform is noteworthy for the marked improvement in the plausibility of the effective polarizability obtained from the submolecule treatment compared with the point dipole approximation [105]. Submolecules are located at the carbon and iodine atoms.
The molecular axes coincide with the crystal axes.

(2) Crystal susceptibilities
Optical susceptibilities are obtained from the refractive indices $n_a = 1.75$ and $n_c = 1.80$.

	$\chi_{aa} = \chi_{bb}$	χ_{cc}	λ
[18]	2.06	2.24	not given

(3) Lorentz-factor tensors [105]

kk'	$L_{aa} = L_{bb}$	L_{cc}
11	0.5164	−0.0328
12	0.0599	0.8801

(4) Polarizability volumes [105]

$\alpha_\perp$	$\alpha_\parallel$
15.6	13.9

3.6.15 Sulphur, S_8

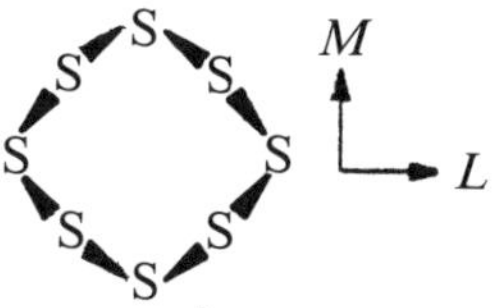

(1) Crystal structure
Space group *Fddd*, with $a = 10.437$, $b = 12.485$, $c = 24.369$ Å, and $Z = 4$ [106]. Submolecules are located at each sulphur atom.
The mean molecular plane makes an angle ϕ with the a axis, where $\phi = \pi/2 + \tan^{-1}(b/a)$ [107].

(2) Crystal susceptibilities

	χ_{aa}	χ_{bb}	χ_{cc}	λ
[108]	2.68	2.81	3.66	589

(3) Lorentz-factor tensors [109]

kk'	L_{aa}	L_{ab}	L_{bb}	L_{cc}
11	0.462	−0.178	0.542	−0.004
12	0.676	0.643	0.538	−0.214
13	0.348	0	0.148	0.504
14	0.074	0	0.154	0.772

(4) Polarizability volumes [109]

α_{LL}	α_{MM}	α_{MN}	α_{NN}
29.4	25.8	0.3	18.5

3.7 NON-LINEAR OPTICS

So far we have assumed that the response in our materials has been linear—for example, that the polarization $\boldsymbol{P}$ is proportional in magnitude to the field which produces it. In general this is not so: $\boldsymbol{P}$ always contains contributions proportional to higher odd powers of the field and sometimes contributions proportional to even powers as well. Such non-linear contributions are typically weak, and have received extensive attention only with the availability of lasers capable of providing intense beams and corresponding to high optical electric fields.

In linear optics, the optical response occurs at the same frequency as the electric field stimulus; the response to several fields is simply the sum of the separate responses. In non-linear optics, the response occurs at various frequencies constructed as multiples of that of a single stimulus or as combinations of those of multiple stimuli. This leads to a wide variety of new phenomena including second and third harmonic generation (frequency doubling and trebling) and refractive indices which depend on an applied electric field (electro-optic effect) or on intensity. Such phenomena are readily applicable in transmitting and processing information, given stable materials with a high enough response at suitable frequencies.

Molecular materials including crystals offer considerable promise for non-linear optics. They can have a high non-linear response which is predominantly electronic in origin and hence rapid, and they can have good resistance to laser damage. Moreover, because their linear and non-linear responses arise directly from the corresponding molecular responses, it should be possible to tailor them by tailoring the molecules. For example, one can envisage using techniques from dye chemistry to ensure that molecules designed for second harmonic generation do not at the same time absorb significantly the second harmonic they are generating.

These considerations have given rise to markedly increased research activity in recent years on non-linear optics of molecular materials, as witness several books and conference proceedings [110–113]. For many applications, polymers are likely to be the materials of choice. However, molecular crystals have been studied not only in bulk form but also as crystalline thin films and crystal-cored fibres. Bulk crystals are particularly useful for bringing out basic principles. These naturally depend on a full understanding of the linear optical behaviour discussed earlier, which is more complicated under the monoclinic symmetry typical of molecular crystals than under the higher symmetries typical of the inorganic ionic and covalent crystals commonly investigated for non-linear optics.

In the present section, our aim is to apply and extend the considerations of previous sections to non-linear optics of molecular crystals. Since accounts of the non-linear optics are paradoxically more commonly available than those of the linear optics, our treatment is designed to provide a bridge to advanced accounts rather than an exhaustive account. We concentrate on the phenomena of second-harmonic generation and the Pockels or linear electro-optic effect, which are both quadratic non-linearities.

Macroscopically, non-linear response is characterized by expanding the polarization $\boldsymbol{P}$ as a power series in macroscopic electric field $\boldsymbol{E}$:

$$P_i/\varepsilon_0 = \chi_{ij}E_j + \chi_{ijk}E_jE_k + \chi_{ijkl}E_jE_kE_l + \cdots \tag{3.7.1}$$

Here an abbreviated notation is used in which the composite latin subscripts i, j, k, l denote a cartesian subscript *and* an associated frequency [114]. Repeated subscripts are understood to be summed over the Greek cartesian components α, β, etc., so that

$$\chi_{ij}E_j = \sum_{\beta} \chi_{\alpha\beta}(\omega_0;\ \omega_0)E_\beta(\omega_0), \tag{3.7.2}$$

where $\chi_{\alpha\beta}(\omega_0;\ \omega_0)$ is the linear susceptibility, showing the first (output) frequency to be the same as the second (input) frequency; often the output frequency is shown as negative. The χ_{ijk} are components of the quadratic susceptibility tensor $\boldsymbol{\chi}^{(2)}$, the χ_{ijkl} those of the cubic susceptibility tensor $\boldsymbol{\chi}^{(3)}$, and so on. In each case, the output frequency associated with subscript i must equal the sum of the input frequencies associated with subscripts $j, k,\ldots$ (which may be positive or negative, from the complex exponential representation of sin ωt giving the time dependence of a real electric field). Second-harmonic generation or SHG corresponds to $\omega_1 = \omega_2 = \omega$ and $\omega_0 = 2\omega$; the linear electro-optic effect to $\omega_1 = \omega$, $\omega_2 = 0$ (i.e. a static electric field) and $\omega_0 = \omega$. In both these cases, the coefficients customarily used to describe the phenomenon are not simply the components of the relevant quadratic susceptibility itself.

In the general expression (3.7.1), output at the sum frequency $\omega_1 + \omega_2$ of two electric fields $\boldsymbol{E}(\omega_1)$ and $\boldsymbol{E}(\omega_2)$ arises from *two* sets of terms in which $\boldsymbol{E}(\omega_1)$ either precedes or follows $\boldsymbol{E}(\omega_2)$. Naturally symmetry requires that the corresponding susceptibilities are equal. To avoid discontinuities in the limit when ω_1 becomes equal to ω_2, one retains two sets of terms for SHG, even though these have become identical in form as well as magnitude. On the other hand, the customary expression for SHG has

$$P_\alpha(2\omega)/\varepsilon_0 = \sum_{\beta\gamma} d_{\alpha\beta\gamma}E^0_\beta(\omega)E^0_\gamma(\omega), \tag{3.7.3}$$

where now the E_0 are field amplitudes with no duplication of terms, so that overall [115] $d_{\alpha\beta\gamma} = \frac{1}{2}\chi_{\alpha\beta\gamma}(2\omega;\ \omega, \omega)$. It is also customary to use the Voigt abbreviated notation for the pair of indices $\beta\gamma$ in $d_{\alpha\beta\gamma}$ so that $(11) \to 1$, $(22) \to 2$, $(33) \to 3$, $(23) \to 4$, $(31) \to 5$, $(12) \to 6$. Thus $d_{111} \to d_{11}$, $d_{122} \to d_{12}$, $d_{123} \to d_{14}$, and so on.

The linear electro-optic effect is usually characterized as the electric field dependence of the optical indicatrix ϵ^{-1} (Section 3.2) in terms of the coefficient

$$r_{\alpha\beta\gamma} = \partial\epsilon^{-1}_{\alpha\beta}/\partial E_\gamma \tag{3.7.4}$$

$$= -\epsilon^{-1}_{\alpha\lambda}(\partial\epsilon_{\lambda\mu}/\partial E_\gamma)\epsilon^{-1}_{\mu\beta}. \tag{3.7.5}$$

Since $\epsilon = \boldsymbol{1} + \boldsymbol{\chi}^{(1)}$, the derivative in equation (3.7.5) is $\chi_{\lambda\mu\gamma}$. In the principal axis system of the indicatrix (at zero field), one obtains

$$r_{\alpha\beta\gamma} = -\chi_{\alpha\beta\gamma}(\omega;\ \omega, 0)/n^2_\alpha n^2_\beta, \tag{3.7.6}$$

where n_α is the principal refractive index for direction α, and now α and β are not summed. Depending on how the electric fields are defined, there may be a factor 2 on the right-hand side. In the electro-optic effect the pair of indices $\alpha\beta$ in $r_{\alpha\beta\gamma}$ is customarily abbreviated using the Voigt notation, so that $r_{111} \rightarrow r_{11}, r_{112} \rightarrow r_{12}, r_{123} \rightarrow r_{63}$, and so on. Note that both uses of the Voigt notation apply it to two indices referring to the same frequency.

For second-harmonic generation, two aspects of linear optics are important. The first is *phase matching*. As the beam of light at the fundamental frequency ω propagates through the crystal, it generates light at the second-harmonic frequency 2ω all along its path. This light propagates too, but in general it does so with a different refractive index and hence speed. The result is that at a given point the second-harmonic wave will be a superposition of waves generated at different points which will therefore have different phases. Such waves will interfere, limiting the second-harmonic intensity achievable. Maximum intensity will be achieved in a crystal thickness of one *coherence length* l_{coh}, given by

$$l_{\text{coh}} = \lambda/4(n_{2\omega} - n_{\omega}), \tag{3.7.7}$$

where λ is the wavelength of the harmonic. Hence one seeks to maximize the second-harmonic intensity by making the harmonic and second-harmonic refractive indices equal. Various means of achieving this are available in anisotropic crystals with suitable optical properties [116], making use of the existence of both ordinary and extraordinary rays for a given frequency.

The other important factor is *walk-off*. As we saw in Section 3.2, the displacement $\boldsymbol{D}$ and the electric field $\boldsymbol{E}$ make an angle ξ in a crystal, and the same angle is made between the ray direction and the propagation direction. Hence waves which propagate collinearly to maximize the region over which they interact may correspond to rays which diverge and thereby limit the size of this region. However, the considerations of Section 3.2 also show that one can find special directions in which the walk-off angle is zero, i.e. where the energy and phase propagate collinearly too.

Non-linear susceptibilities exhibit various symmetries. As implied by the notation of equation (3.7.1), the coefficients χ_{ijk} are invariant under interchange of subscripts j and k, i.e. under interchange of cartesian components with their associated frequencies. For second-harmonic generation, the frequencies are equal anyway, and hence $\chi_{\alpha\beta\gamma}$ for SHG is symmetric under interchange of cartesian components β and γ. Similarly, since the optical indicatrix is symmetric, $\chi_{\alpha\beta\gamma}$ for the linear electro-optic effect is symmetric under interchange of cartesian components α and β. At zero frequency, $\chi_{\alpha\beta\gamma}$ is symmetric under any permutation of $\alpha\beta\gamma$. This symmetry is often approximately observed even at non-zero frequencies, provided these are not close to an absorption frequency, and is termed *Kleinman symmetry* [117].

In centrosymmetric crystals, all components of $\boldsymbol{\chi}^{(2)}$ and other even-order susceptibilities vanish. Under inversion, the polarization must change sign while products of even numbers of electric fields in equation (3.7.1) must be unchanged. This can be satisfied only if $\boldsymbol{\chi}^{(2n)} = 0$. In practice, most molecular crystals adopt centrosymmetric structures, with only about 25% lacking a centre of symmetry [118]. This leads to various strategies to force or encourage non-centrosymmetry. Chiral molecules cannot adopt centrosymmetric space groups, for example. Hydrogen bonding may favour non-centrosymmetry, as may bulky groups which give molecules an 'awkward' shape. However, although achieving non-centrosymmetry is necessary for achieving a non-zero $\chi^{(2)}$, it is not sufficient to make $\chi^{(2)}$ large. This depends in more detail on the properties of the molecules and their arrangement in the crystal.

Crystal non-linear response arises from the molecular non-linear response. Corresponding to the macroscopic equation (3.7.1) there is the microscopic equation

$$\boldsymbol{p}_i = \alpha_{ij}\boldsymbol{F}_j + \beta_{ijk}\boldsymbol{F}_j\boldsymbol{F}_k + \gamma_{ijkl}\boldsymbol{F}_j\boldsymbol{F}_k\boldsymbol{F}_l + \cdots \tag{3.7.8}$$

In addition to the usual linear response to the local field $\boldsymbol{F}$ through the polarizability $\boldsymbol{\alpha}$, there is non-linear response through the first and second *hyperpolarizabilities* $\boldsymbol{\beta}$ and $\boldsymbol{\gamma}$. These depend on symmetry in the same way as the macroscopic susceptibilities: $\boldsymbol{\alpha}$ and $\boldsymbol{\gamma}$ are always non-zero, but $\boldsymbol{\beta}$ is non-zero only in non-centrosymmetric molecules. Fortunately there is no difficulty in making $\boldsymbol{\beta}$ non-zero, although as with $\chi^{(2)}$ this need not make $\boldsymbol{\beta}$ large. In practice, high hyperpolarizability is achieved in molecules which contain donor and acceptor groups linked by a conjugated pathway. Typical donors are based on the amino group $-NH_2$, while acceptors often contain the nitro group $-NO_2$. The conjugated pathway is usually constructed from one or more aromatic or heteroaromatic rings and alkene groups [119].

Crystal and molecular non-linear response can be related by a development of the arguments already presented for linear response. The key is again to relate the local field to the macroscopic field. We can still use equation (3.5.3) relating the local field $\boldsymbol{F}_k$ at molecule $\boldsymbol{k}$ to the macroscopic field $\boldsymbol{E}$ and the induced dipole moments $\boldsymbol{p}_k$ via the Lorentz-factor tensors $\boldsymbol{L}_{kk'}$. However, the $\boldsymbol{p}_{k'}$ are now related to the local fields by (3.7.9), so that

$$\boldsymbol{F}_k = \boldsymbol{E} + \sum_{k'} \boldsymbol{L}_{kk'} \cdot (\alpha_{k'} \cdot \boldsymbol{F}_{k'} + \boldsymbol{\beta}_{k'} \colon \boldsymbol{F}_{k'}\boldsymbol{F}_{k'} + \gamma_{k'} \vdots \boldsymbol{F}_{k'}\boldsymbol{F}_{k'}\boldsymbol{F}_{k'} + \cdots)/\varepsilon_0 v, \tag{3.7.9}$$

where for simplicity all explicit frequency dependence has been suppressed. By solving the linear local field problem as before, we obtain

$$\boldsymbol{F}_k = \boldsymbol{d}_k \cdot \boldsymbol{E} + \sum_{k''k'} \boldsymbol{D}_{kk'} \cdot \boldsymbol{L}_{k'k''} \cdot (\boldsymbol{b}_{k''} \colon \boldsymbol{F}_{k''}\boldsymbol{F}_{k'} + \boldsymbol{c}_{k''} \vdots \boldsymbol{F}_{k''}\boldsymbol{F}_{k''}\boldsymbol{F}_{k''} + \cdots), \tag{3.7.10}$$

with $\boldsymbol{b} = \boldsymbol{\beta}/\varepsilon_0 v$ and $\boldsymbol{c} = \boldsymbol{\gamma}/\varepsilon_0 v$. There is no explicit solution for $\boldsymbol{F}_k$ in terms of $\boldsymbol{E}$, but a solution accurate to desired order in $\boldsymbol{E}$ can be obtained by iteration. This suffices to determine the $\chi^{(n)}$ to the same order. Details of the solution, which is rather complicated, are given elsewhere [120, 121]. As equation (3.7.10) shows, with non-linear response the local field is no longer a linear function of the macroscopic field: in general, it contains terms of all orders.

Using the final result for the local field in equation (3.7.8), substituting in equation (3.5.1) to obtain the polarization from the induced dipole moments, and then comparing coefficients of powers of $\boldsymbol{E}$ with equation (3.7.1) yields microscopic expressions for the $\chi^{(n)}$. One obtains the linear susceptibility $\chi^{(1)}$ as in equation (3.5.14). The quadratic susceptibility is [122]

$$\chi^{(2)}(\omega_0;\ \omega_1, \omega_2) = \sum_k \boldsymbol{b}_k(\omega_0;\ \omega_1, \omega_2) \vdots \boldsymbol{d}_k(\omega_0)\boldsymbol{d}_k(\omega_1)\boldsymbol{d}_k(\omega_2), \qquad (3.7.11)$$

where, as previously, improved results may be obtained by averaging over submolecules j as well as summing over sublattices k. The cubic susceptibility comprises two contributions [123]. The *direct* contribution is the analogue of $\chi^{(2)}$ [102]:

$$\chi^{(3d)}(\omega_0;\ \omega_1, \omega_2, \omega_3) = \sum_k \boldsymbol{c}_k(\omega_0;\ \omega_1, \omega_2, \omega_3) :: \boldsymbol{d}_k(\omega_0)\boldsymbol{d}_k(\omega_1)\boldsymbol{d}_k(\omega_2)\boldsymbol{d}_k(\omega_3). \qquad (3.7.12)$$

However, there is also a *cascading* contribution arising from the mixed quadratic response to that part of the local field quadratic in the macroscopic field as well as that part linear in the macroscopic field [102]:

$$\chi^{(3c)} = 2 \sum_{kk'k''} \boldsymbol{b}_k(\omega_0;\ \omega_1, \omega_4) \vdots \boldsymbol{d}_k(\omega_0)\boldsymbol{d}_k(\omega_1)\boldsymbol{D}_{kk'}(\omega_4) \cdot \boldsymbol{L}_{k'k''} \cdot \boldsymbol{b}_{k''}(\omega_4;\ \omega_2, \omega_3) \vdots \boldsymbol{d}_{k''}(\omega_2)\boldsymbol{d}_{k''}(\omega_3), \qquad (3.7.13)$$

where $\omega_4 = \omega_2 + \omega_3$ and hence $\omega_0 = \omega_1 + \omega_4 = \omega_1 + \omega_2 + \omega_3$ as required.

Few attempts have been made to use the full form of these equations, and $\chi^{(3)}$ has been little studied theoretically at all. Most often, the local field tensors have been replaced by the Lorentz approximation (3.4.9) using the average linear susceptibility; sometimes the anisotropic version (3.4.17) has been used instead. If we set $\boldsymbol{d}_k(\omega) \approx d^{\mathrm{L}}(\omega)\boldsymbol{1}$, then $\chi^{(2)}$ becomes

$$\chi^{(2)}(\omega_0;\ \omega_1, \omega_2) = d^{\mathrm{L}}(\omega_0)d^{\mathrm{L}}(\omega_1)d^{\mathrm{L}}(\omega_2) \sum_k \boldsymbol{b}_k(\omega_0;\ \omega_1, \omega_2). \qquad (3.7.14)$$

In this approximation, the local fields are merely scalar factors which enhance the magnitude of $\chi^{(2)}$. The principal origin of $\chi^{(2)}$ is then ascribed to the net hyperpolarizability of the unit cell in the crystal axes. This shows at once how $\chi^{(2)}$ vanishes in centrosymmetric crystals where the $\boldsymbol{b}_k$ are equal and opposite in pairs. It also allows the role of molecular orientation to be isolated and explored.

At least in the smaller molecules of interest for non-linear optics, there is typically a single dominant electronic transition reflecting charge transfer from the donor to the acceptor group. Frequently the chromophores are coplanar, the dipole moment of this transition lies in the given plane, and the contribution of the transition to the polarizability and hyperpolarizability is said to be two-dimensional. Sometimes the chromophores are collinear, giving a transition dipole moment along the given axis and a one-dimensional contribution to the molecular response. For these cases one may explore the resultant behaviour of $\chi^{(2)}$ in different crystal classes in terms of the angles between the transition moment and the molecular and crystal axes [124]. The analysis provides relationships between the components of the unit-cell hyperpolarizabilities in the crystal axes in terms of the orientation of the transition moment, and these relationships allow one to analyse experimental susceptibilities to test how closely the one-dimensional or two-dimensional approximation is satisfied. In addition, the analysis yields optimum orientations in which the molecular non-linearity gives a maximum crystal non-linearity [125].

The full expressions (3.7.11) for $\chi^{(2)}$ and (3.7.12) and (3.7.13) for $\chi^{(3)}$ have been applied to a few well studied crystals using molecular-orbital calculations of hyperpolarizabilities as input. Calculations for *meta*- and *para*-nitroaniline (mNA and pNA) [122, 127] illustrate the sort of results obtainable. The local fields in mNA are found to differ in anisotropy from those given by the anisotropic Lorentz approximation, and have sizeable off-diagonal elements. The latter feature means that many elements of the molecular hyperpolarizability $\boldsymbol{\beta}$ may contribute to $\chi^{(2)}$, with the possibility of significant contributions not included in the purely geometrical approach just outlined. The resulting components of $\chi^{(2)}$ for SHG in mNA are in broad agreement with experiment and show that deviations from Kleinman symmetry are mostly within 10%.

Being centrosymmetric, the pNA crystal has zero $\chi^{(2)}$, but its $\chi^{(3)}$ can be compared with that for mNA [128]. The direct and cascading contributions are both larger for pNA, reflecting its larger $\boldsymbol{\beta}$ and $\boldsymbol{\gamma}$. For both pNA and mNA, the cascading contribution can be 5% or more of the total; since this contribution varies as the square of $\boldsymbol{\beta}$, it could easily be a larger fraction of the total in crystals with higher $\boldsymbol{\beta}$, unless $\boldsymbol{\gamma}$ increases faster than the square of $\boldsymbol{\beta}$. The result for mNA and pNA suggest that a centrosymmetric structure may enhance $\chi^{(3d)}$ at the expense of $\chi^{(3c)}$, but much work remains to be done to understand better the factors influencing $\chi^{(3)}$ including $\boldsymbol{\gamma}$ itself. At present, much the largest values of $\chi^{(3)}$ are found for polymers, such as some polydiacetylenes [127].

3.8 REFERENCES

1. F. S. Crawford, *Waves, Berkeley Physics Course*, Volume III, McGraw-Hill, New York, 1968.
2. E. M. Purcell, *Electricity and Magnetism, Berkeley Physics Course*, Volume II, McGraw-Hill, New York, 1966.
3. R. P. Feynman, R. B. Leighton and M. Sands, *Feynman Lectures on Physics*, Freeman, San Francisco, 1963.
4. J. F. Nye, *Physical Properties of Crystals*, Clarendon, Oxford, 1957.
5. M. Born and E. Wolf, *Principles of Optics*, 4th edition, Pergamon, Oxford, 1968.

6. H. J. Juretschke, *Crystal Physics*, Benjamin, Reading, MA, 1974.
7. J. W. Rohleder and T. Luty, *Mol. Cryst. Liq. Cryst.*, **5** (1968) 145.
8. N. W. Hartshorne and A. Stuart, *Crystals and the Polarizing Microscope*, 4th edition, Edward Arnold, London, 1970.
9. A. Hinchliffe and R. W. Munn, *Molecular Electromagnetism*, Wiley, Chichester, 1985.
10. W. Wardzyński, *Acta Phys. Polon.*, **A39** (1971) 21; *Proc. Roy. Soc. Lond.*, **A260** (1961) 370.
11. J. W. Rohleder and M. Kucharska, *Rocz. Chem.*, **47** (1973) 389.
12. R. Verreault, *Z. Krist.*, **136** (1952) 350.
13. T. Luty, A. Mierzejewski and R. W. Munn, *Chem. Phys.*, **29** (1978) 353; R. W. Munn, T. Luty and A. Mierzejewski, *Chem. Phys.*, **34** (1978) 1; R. W. Munn and T. Luty, *Chem. Phys.*, **39** (1979) 303.
14. W. Kusto and J. W. Rohleder, *Mol. Cryst. Liq. Cryst.*, **51** (1979) 215.
15. N. Wiser, *Phys. Rev.*, **129** (1963) 62.
16. R. W. Munn, *Chem. Phys.*, **50** (1980) 119; R. W. Munn and T. Luty, *Chem. Phys.*, **81** (1983) 41; L. M. Hafkenscheid and J. Vlieger, *Physica*, **75** (1974) 57.
17. W. Rousset, *La Diffusion de la Lumière par les Molécules Rigides*, Paris, 1947.
18. A. N. Winchell, *The Optical Properties of Organic Compounds*, 2nd edition, Academic Press, New York, 1954.
19. R. J. W. Le Fèvre, *Advances in Physical Organic Chemistry*, Volume III, Academic Press, London, 1965.
20. M. Atoji and R. E. Rundle, *J. Chem. Phys.*, **29** (1958) 1306.
21. Landolt-Börnstein, *Zahlenwerte und Funktionen*, Volume 2, Part 8 (1962), Section 2–76.
22. J. W. Rohleder, *Rocz. Chem.*, **46** (1972) 2089.
23. S. P. Liebmann and J. W. Moskowitz, *J. Chem. Phys.*, **54** (1971) 3622.
24. M. Born and W. Heisenberg, *Z. Phys.*, **23** (1924) 388; *Gmelins Handbuch der Anorganischen Chemie*, 8th edition, System No. 28, Part A, Lief. 2 (1957), p. 386.
25. C. J. F. Böttcher, *Rec. Trav. Chim.*, **65** (1946) 14; *Gmelins Handbuch der Anorganischen Chemie*, l.c., System No. 9, Lief. 2 (1960), p. 639.
26. M. A. Lasheen and A. M. Abdeen, *Acta Cryst.*, **A28** (1972) 245.
27. M. A. Lasheen and I. H. Ibrahim, *Acta Cryst.*, **A31** (1975) 136.
28. M. S. Farag, *Acta Cryst.*, **7** (1954) 117.
29. H. W. W. Ehrlich, *Acta Cryst.*, **10** (1957) 699.
30. P. Groth, *Chemische Kristallographie*, Engelmann, Leipzig, 1919.
31. Y. Okaya and R. Pepinsky, *Acta Cryst.*, **10** (1957) 324.
32. Y. Okaya, *Acta Cryst.*, **19** (1965) 879.
33. J. Trotter, *Acta. Cryst.*, **14** (1961) 244, 1135.
34. C. J. Brown and D. E. C. Corbridge, *Acta Cryst.*, **7** (1954) 711.
35. C. J. Brown, *Proc. Roy. Soc.*, **A302** (1968) 185.
36. R. N. Brown, *Acta Cryst.*, **14** (1961) 711.
37. A. J. Van Bommel and J. M. Bijvoet, *Acta Cryst.*, **11** (1958) 61.
38. D. W. J. Cruickshank, *Acta Cryst.*, **9** (1956) 915.
39. A Hargreaves and H. Hasan Rizvi, *Acta Cryst.*, **15** (1962) 365.
40. A. Tulinsky and J. C. White, *Acta Cryst.*, **11** (1958) 7.
41. U Croatto, S. Bezzi and E. Bua, *Acta Cryst.*, **5** (1952) 825.
42. B. V. R. Murty, *Z. Kristallogr.*, **113** (1960) 445.
43. S. S. C. Chu, G. A. Jeffrey and T. Sakurai, *Acta Cryst.*, **15** (1962) 661.
44. T. Sakurai, *Acta Cryst.*, **15** (1962) 443.
45. K. N. Trueblood, E. Goldish and J. Donohue, *Acta Cryst.*, **14** (1961) 1009.
46. G. H. Goldschmidt and F. J. Llewellyn, *Acta Cryst.*, **3** (1950) 294.
47. D. J. Sutor, *Acta Cryst.*, **11** (1958) 83.

48. G. M. Brown, H. G. Norment and H. A. Levy, *Acta Cryst.*, **10** (1957) 806.
49. D. R. Davies and J. J. Blum, *Acta Cryst.*, **8** (1955) 129.
50. D. A. Dunmur, *Mol. Phys.*, **23** (1972) 109.
51. P. P. Ewald, *Ann. Phys.*, **64** (1921) 253.
52. M. Born and M. Bradburn, *Proc. Cambridge Phil. Soc.*, **39** (1943) 104.
53. P. G. Cummins, D. A. Dunmur and R. W. Munn, *Chem. Phys. Lett.*, **22** (1973) 519.
54. P. G. Cummins, D. A. Dunmur and R. W. Munn, *Chem. Phys. Lett.*, **36** (1975) 199.
55. T. Luty, *Chem. Phys. Lett.*, **44** (1976) 335.
56. F. P. Chen, D. M. Hanson and D. Fox, *Chem. Phys. Lett.*, **30** (1975) 337.
57. P. J. Bounds and R. W. Munn, *Chem. Phys.*, **24** (1977) 343.
58. J. H. Meyling, P. J. Bounds and R. W. Munn, *Chem. Phys. Lett.*, **51** (1977) 234.
59. R. W. Munn and T. Luty, *Chem. Phys.*, **38** (1979) 413.
60. T. Luty and R. W. Munn, *Chem. Phys.*, **43** (1979) 295.
61. T. Luty, A. Mierzejewski and R. W. Munn, *Chem. Phys.*, **29** (1978) 353.
62. R. W. Munn and T. Luty, *Chem. Phys.*, **39** (1979) 303.
63. R. W. Munn, T. Luty and A. Mierzejewski, *Chem. Phys.*, **34** (1978) 1.
64. S. D. Druger and R. S. Knox, *J. Chem. Phys.*, **50** (1969) 3143.
65. D. A. Dunmur and R. W. Munn, *Chem. Phys.*, **11** (1975) 297.
66. P. J. Bounds and R. W. Munn, *Chem. Phys.*, **44** (1979) 103.
67. D. Fox, *Chem. Phys.*, **17** (1967) 273; F. P. Chen, D. M. Hanson and D. Fox, *J. Chem. Phys.*, **66** (1977) 4954.
68. R. W. Munn, *Chem. Phys.*, **76** (1983) 243.
69. R. W. Munn and I. Eisenstein, *J. Phys. A: Math. Gen.*, **16** (1983) 2853.
70. E. A. Silinsh, *Organic Molecular Crystals: Their Electronic States*, Springer, Berlin, 1980.
71. P. J. Bounds and R. W. Munn, *Chem. Phys.*, **59** (1981) 41.
72. P. J. Bounds and R. W. Munn, *Chem. Phys.*, **59** (1981) 47.
73. I. Eisenstein, R. W. Munn and P. J. Bounds, *Chem. Phys.*, **74** (1983) 307.
74. I. Eisenstein and R. W. Munn, *Chem. Phys.*, **77** (1983) 47.
75. I. Eisenstein and R. W. Munn, *Chem. Phys.*, **79** (1983) 189.
76. P. J. Bounds, W. Siebrand, I. Eisenstein, R. W. Munn and P. Petelenz, *Chem. Phys.*, **95** (1985) 197.
77. E. G. Cox, D. W. J. Cruickshank and J. A. S. Smith, *Proc. Roy. Soc. Lond.*, **A247** (1958) 1.
78. R. Gay and B. Lemanceau, *Cahiers Phys.*, **74** (1956) 38.
79. D. W. J. Cruickshank, *Acta Cryst.*, **10** (1957) 504.
80. R. Mason, *Mol. Phys.*, **4** (1961) 413.
81. D. W. J. Cruickshank, *Acta Cryst.*, **9** (1956) 915.
82. K. S. Sundararajan, *Z. Kristallogr.*, **93** (1936) 238.
83. J. M. Robertson and J. G. White, *J. Chem. Soc.* (1947) 358; A. Camerman and J. Trotter, *Acta Cryst.*, **18** (1965) 636.
84. A. H. Price, J. O. Williams and R. W. Munn, *Chem. Phys.*, **14** (1976) 413.
85. C. J. Spicer, Ph.D. Thesis, UMIST (1986).
86. H. M. Rietveld, E. N. Maslen and C. J. B. Clews, *Acta Cryst.*, **B26** (1970) 693.
87. J. H. Meyling, W. H. Hesselink and D. A. Wiersma, *Chem. Phys.*, **17** (1976) 353.
88. M. Hurst and R. W. Munn, unpublished results.
89. A. C. Skapski and J. L. Stevenson, *J. Chem. Soc. Perkin 2* (1973) 1197.
90. M. Hurst and R. W. Munn, *J. Mol. Electronics*, **2** (1987) 139.
91. J. G. Bergman and G. R. Crane, *J. Chem. Phys.*, **66** (1977) 3803.
92. R. E. Long, R. A. Sparks and K. N. Trueblood, *Acta Cryst.*, **18** (1965) 932.
93. R. J. Phillips, PhD Thesis, UMIST (1987).

94. R. R. Pennelly and C. J. Eckhardt, *Chem. Phys.*, **12** (1976) 89; J. Merski and C. J. Eckhardt, *J. Chem. Phys.*, **75** (1981) 3731.
95. S. Aravamudhan, U. Haeberlen, E. H. Ingartinger and C. Krieger, *Mol. Phys.*, **38** (1979) 241.
96. C. J. Eckhardt and J. Merski, *Surf. Sci.*, **37** (1973) 937; J. Merski and C. J. Eckhardt, *J. Chem. Phys.*, **75** (1981) 3705.
97. L. J. Soltzberg, P. A. Piliero and M. R. O'Shea, *Mol. Cryst. Liq. Cryst.*, **29** (1974) 151.
98. W. J. Kusto and J. W. Rohleder, *Mol. Cryst. Liq. Cryst.*, **55** (1979) 151.
99. A. Hinchliffe, R. W. Munn and C. J. Spicer, *Mol. Cryst. Liq. Cryst.*, **73** (1981) 181.
100. A. Caron and J. Donohue, *Acta Cryst.*, **17** (1964) 544.
101. J. M. Halbout, S. Blit, W. Donaldson and C. L. Tang, *IEEE J. Quantum Electron.*, **QE-15** (1979) 1176.
102. M. Hurst and R. W. Munn, *J. Mol. Electronics*, **3** (1987) 75.
103. T. L. Khotsyanova, A. I. Kitaigorodskii and Y. Struchkov, *Zh. Fiz. Khim.*, **27** (1953) 647.
104. Y. Iwata and T. Watanabe, *Ann. Rep. Res. React. Inst. Kyoto Univ.*, **7** (1974) 87.
105. R. W. Munn and S. M. Bourne, *Chem. Phys. Lett.*, **75** (1980) 403.
106. S. C. Abrahams, *Acta Cryst.*, **8** (1955) 661.
107. I. Chen, *Phys. Rev.*, **B2** (1970) 1060.
108. P. G. Cummins, PhD Thesis, University of Sheffield (1974); W. Schmidt, *Ann. Phys. (Leipzig),* **11** (1903) 114.
109. P. J. Bounds and R. W. Munn, *Chem. Phys.*, **39** (1979) 165.
110. D. J. Williams, ed., *Nonlinear Optical Properties of Organic and Polymer Materials*, ACS Symposium Series No. 233, American Chemical Society, Washington, DC, 1983.
111. J. Zyss, *J. Mol. Electronics*, **1** (1985) 25.
112. D. S. Chemla and J. Zyss, eds, *Nonlinear Optical Properties of Organic Molecules and Crystals*, 2 vols., Academic Press, New York, 1987.
113. R. A. Hann and D. Bloor, eds, *Organic Materials for Nonlinear Optics*, RSC Special Publication No. 69, Royal Society of Chemistry, London, 1989.
114. R. W. Munn, *J. Mol. Electronics*, **4** (1988) 31.
115. Y. R. Shen, *The Principles of Nonlinear Optics*, Wiley, New York, 1984.
116. M. V. Hobden, *J. Appl. Phys.*, **38** (1967) 4365.
117. D. A. Kleinman, *Phys. Rev.*, **126** (1962) 1977.
118. J. F. Nicoud and R. J. Twieg, in ref. 112, vol. 1, p. 227.
119. D. Pugh and J. O. Morley, in ref. 112, vol. 1, p. 193.
120. J. A. Armstrong, N. Bloembergen, J. Ducuing and P. S. Pershan, *Phys. Rev.*, **127** (1962) 1918.
121. M. Hurst and R. W. Munn, *J. Mol. Electronics*, **2** (1986) 35.
122. M. Hurst and R. W. Munn, *J. Mol. Electronics*, **2** (1986) 139.
123. G. R. Meredith, B. Buchalter and C. Hanzlik, *J. Chem. Phys.*, **78** (1983) 6865.
124. J. Zyss and D. S. Chemla, in ref. 112, vol. 1, p. 23.
125. J. L. Oudar and J. Zyss, *Phys. Rev.*, **A26** (1982) 2016; J. Zyss and J. L. Oudar, *Phys. Rev.*, **A26** (1982) 2028.
126. C. Sauteret, J.-P. Hermann, R. Frey, F. Pradère, J. Ducuing, R. H. Baughman and R. R. Chance, *Phys. Rev. Lett.*, **36** (1976) 956.
127. M. Hurst and R. W. Munn, in ref. 113, p. 3.

Subject Index

Chemical Substance Index